THE GEOLOGY OF

Front cover: The cliffs at Kilve display fossil-rich Lower Jurassic limestones and shales which are cut through by regular patterns of joints and occasional faults.

Back cover: The Lower Jurassic ammonite *Caloceras johnstoni* is preserved in beautiful mother of pearl colours in the fine-granied sediments on the coast at Watchet.

This cliff face at Burrington Coombe is cut by a striking bed of dolomitic limestone of Carboniferous age.

The GEOLOGY of SOMERSET

Peter Hardy

EX LIBRIS PRESS

Published in 1999 by
EX LIBRIS PRESS
1 The Shambles
Bradford on Avon
Wiltshire
BA15 1JS

Design and typesetting by
Ex Libris Press

Cover printed by Shires Press, Trowbridge, Wiltshire

Printed and bound in Britain by
Cromwell Press, Trowbridge, Wiltshire

ISBN 0 948578 42 4

Contents

Dedication

I wish to dedicate this book to my very good friends, Pippa and Frank Hawtin. They have been a constant source of encouragement and inspiration throughout a friendship which spans three decades. It was they who first welcomed me to Somerset, and we have shared many happy days exploring the lesser known parts that others fail to reach! Without their support through some very difficult times, it is doubtful if I should ever have commenced this work. Hasta la vista.

Acknowledgments

There are many people to whom I owe thanks for their encouragement, knowledge, patience and tolerance, and I am sure that they will recognise themselves! My original mentor and tutor Dr. Fred Broadhurst, without whom I would never have studied geology, has remained a good friend for well over thirty years. I thank Prof. Mick Aston, another long term friend, for his encouragement and for offering me the use of his computer which enabled me to produce legible text for an early draft, and for the loan of several of his photographs. I am indebted to Chris Harris for her constant support, advice on many aspects of the content of the book and for patiently reading and editing my quaint grammar.

I wish to thank the British Geological Survey for their cooperation in permitting the tracing of information from the geological maps of the region and also some sections from the maps and their memoirs. Please note that in re-drawing these any errors introduced are my own, not those of the B.G.S. These reproductions, based on the official maps, are included here by permission of the British Geological Survey, ©NERC. All rights reserved.

I gratefully acknowledge the cooperation of the owners of many quarries and other sites visited during the last thirty years and in my preparations for this work, notably: the owners of the Doulting stone quarry, Keinton Mandeville stone quarry, the farmer at Luxborough, Lime Kiln Hill Quarry (Mells), Foster Yeoman for access to Merehead Quarry and the owners and manager of Moons Hill Quarry, Stoke St. Michael. The management and staff of Hanson Aggregates (formerly ARC) at Whatley have also been very helpful in allowing access to their property in Vallis Vale and permission to use photographs taken there. I am very grateful to the owners of the Banwell Bone Cave, Mr. and Mrs. Haynes and Mr. and Mrs. Sargent for permission to visit and take photographs. I also thank Paul Elkin at Bath Royal Literary and Scientific Institution for the opportunity to photograph the fish from Ilminster. To my publisher, Roger Jones, I can only say 'Sorry for the procrastination and thank you for your fortitude'. Lastly, I would like to thank all those around me who have had to put up with my moods and mess for so long. As for the result of all this assistance, I claim personal responsibility for any mistakes and hope to be forgiven any liability for them.

STRATIGRAPHIC COLUMN

ERA (Mlillions of Years)	SUB-ERA	PERIOD/EPOCH	AGE AT BASE
CAINOZOIC	QUATERNARY	HOLOCENE	.01 (= 10,000 YRS)
		PLEISTOCENE	2
	TERTIARY	PLIOCENE	5
		MIOCENE	24
		OLIGOCENE	42
		EOCENE	58
		PALEOCENE	64
MESOZOIC		CRETACEOUS	135
		JURASSIC	204
		TRIASSIC	250
PALAEOZOIC		PERMIAN	295*
		CARBONIFEROUS	360
		DEVONIAN	408
		SILURIAN	435**
		ORDOVICIAN	510
		CAMBRIAN	545
PRE-CAMBRIAN			

* This date is approximately the time at which the Hercynian Orogeny uplifted the area. There are no rocks of this age preserved locally.

** The oldest rocks in Somerset are the volcanics of the Mendip Hills. These are about 427 million years old.

Fig. 1: The stratigraphical table shows the relationship between rocks of different Periods, and their approximate ages in millions of years (Ma). The information has been derived from the Geological Society's stratigraphical atlas of the British Isles.

Introduction

The main purpose of this book is to enable anyone who might have an interest in the county to understand how it came into being over a very considerable period of geological time, and through many changes of environment. It is not intended that every detail will be covered, nor every corner of the county mentioned, (forgive me if yours is not highlighted) but I hope that you will find there is something about your area, and if it's not mentioned here, then perhaps when you have read this book you could write an article about it yourself! The intention is to explain the scenery of the county of Somerset in terms of its geology in as straightforward a way as possible, and in language that does not require a special knowledge of geology, a subject which is normally fraught with terminology and trendy 'buzzwords', most of which are studiously omitted from this text. Inevitably though, there will be some unfamiliar words and names, so this introduction sets out to explain a few of these. There is a Glossary of terms as well, so please refer to this when necessary.

Somerset is such a large area with so many diverse regions that it is not obvious where to start. However, geologists start at the bottom and work up, so for them it is easy, find the oldest rocks and explain them, then the next younger and so on. This way we build up a picture of the changing geological environment, Period by Period, so that we have a geological history. This makes the choice of starting point easy, providing that you already know the county geologically of course! It has to be the area with the oldest rocks. But how do we know which are the oldest?

The concept of age in rocks may seem to be an easy one; in simple terms there are old rocks and very old rocks. This was more or less the level of appreciation of the age of rocks until the latter half of the 19th century, but thanks to scientific progress, it is now possible to put actual numbers of years to rocks, with a precision which is sometimes rather hard to believe in. However, we need not be too concerned with numbers. What really matters in understanding geology, as in history, is the sequence of events, and this is usually easy to tell because the general rule is that the oldest rocks are at the bottom of the pile and the youngest at the top. So, you have now just learned the very fundamental 'Law of Superposition', i.e. that the younger rocks lie over the older rocks. Geologists are usually quite straightforward people, as this 'Law' demonstrates rather well!

The concept of age of a rock

We cannot rely on a single bed of rock as an indicator of time in a series of localities, but must look for other more reliable chronometers. The first person to find a foolproof one and recognise it should become very famous! In fact there are very few such indicators possible. Imagine what might be suitable in today's world. We could look for the first layers of sediment to contain a polythene bag and say with some confidence that they would not be earlier than around 1950, but I am doubtful if polythene appears in some remote areas of the Earth before the 1970's so this is not an absolutely precise datum. Or we might look for the fall-out from the first atomic bombs and nuclear tests in the 1940's. These traces must be preserved worldwide, albeit in tiny amounts, and could be regarded as almost synchronous. Such indisputable lines of evidence, even in the modern world we know so well, are few enough. Imagine then the difficulty in dealing with the fossil worlds of millions of years ago.

What is the importance of the age of a single bed of rock?

The recognition of ignorance is perhaps the second step towards wisdom. The first step, I would suggest, is the acquisition of enough wisdom to take the second! Therefore, until we recognise that there are limits to what the rocks can and cannot tell us we certainly cannot claim to have derived the complete story from them. If we were to accept that the horizontal strata of rock represent anything more than an environment in one place at one time then we would be presuming something that needs to be proved. It would be as irrational to accept that this was the case as if we believed that a Victorian rubbish tip was the same age as a modern land-fill site just because they were side by side on one level, i.e. the modern ground surface. Clearly the tip has grown over time and thus cannot be synchronous throughout. Similarly, rocks can be deposited over a period of time and may not necessarily be synchronous, even though their sedimentary composition seems not to vary from place to place, even if their fossils do. By way of further analogy we could imagine that the 'glass marble' pop bottles of the Victorian tip, the screw-top returnable bottles of the 1950's and aluminium drinks cans from the late 20th. Century are equivalent to fossils evolving in the sediments. They will evidently occur in separate areas or layers in the tip and can only be mixed together by later disturbance.

Clearly, if you deposit piles of sediment one after another there will be a sequence, starting with the oldest at the bottom. However, there are many things that can interrupt this orderly pile. It might be disturbed by folding, even to the point of being turned upside-down. It can happen that the older rocks are eroded and remnants of them are re-deposited later on in the same section, giving false apparent ages to these lumps of incorporated material. In cases of extreme compression the underlying rocks may be pushed over the younger ones and so reverse the sequence. All of these phenomena occur in rocks in Somerset but in general it is true to say that the older rocks lie under the younger ones and there are relatively few worries about the validity of the vertical sequence, which has remained relatively undisturbed in all but the oldest rocks.

Generally, when geologists establish a sequence of rocks they also produce a geological map of the region. This process requires a great deal of travelling around to record the rocks on a normal topographic map, showing their age, and where possible their type, for example: whether they are sedimentary or igneous. Sorry, here comes the jargon! 'Sedimentary' is easy enough, it simply means materials that were deposited as loose sediment, mud, sand gravel etc., and later became hardened to form rock. 'Igneous' is a derivative from Latin, and means rocks that were created from 'Fire'. In fact there was no actual fire involved in their origins but extreme heat certainly was as these rocks were once melted by it. Most of these rocks cool underground to become solid but some reach the surface and then we see a volcano with its lavas and ashes. Once a map is completed it will be possible to see the relationships between rocks at different localities which will enable us to get an impression of how the region looked at one particular period or, where the rocks cover many different time zones, we can begin to see how the region changed over geological time.

Another well tried geological 'law' is that of *Uniformitarianism*. This rather clumsy word is a very simple way to describe the concept that the events that we witness on the earth today can explain many of the phenomena that rocks demonstrate. For example, it is certainly true that we can observe volcanic eruptions producing vast volumes of lava which, once cooled, looks exactly like many lavas seen in the rock record, even some in Somerset. Similarly, the sands and muds now being deposited on the shores of the Somerset coast in the Bristol Channel are not unlike many of the equivalent rocks found in the geology of the county. From these two examples it becomes clear that in its distant past Somerset was both volcanic and estuarine in turn. However, there are rocks in some parts of the world which almost defy interpretation along these simple lines and clearly had their origins in climates or places which we know little or nothing of. There are also deposits of certain rock types which far exceed in quantity any equivalent ones being formed today. These discrepancies suggest that the balance of environments must have changed dramatically since these rocks were formed. For example, we have enormous areas of Chalk on the borders of Somerset, the modern analogues of which are today only deposited in quite restricted and tropical areas of the globe. The estuarine sediments of the Carboniferous Coal Measures around Radstock are a fraction of a truly enormous ancient swamp which far exceeds any modern river or estuary system. So there have been changes in scale and a few notable major changes in environment over the earlier part of the earth's history but in general, the rocks within the county are perfectly explicable in terms of today's planet and we need not look very far for an answer to the question, 'How did that rock form?'

Incidentally, both of these 'laws', i.e. those of *Superposition* and *Uniformitarianism*, are very early ones in geological science. They were formulated by one of Britain's founding fathers of the subject, James Hutton, in contradiction of the generally held religious belief of his times that the earth had a very short history and had been created in seven days. 'Creationism' was perhaps the last major stand of the non-scientific community against the inevitable progress of scientific knowledge which, in the case of geology, started to break free from religious constraints during the latter half of the 18th and the whole of the 19th Centuries. Some people still adhere to 'Creationism' of course, but the scientific community has moved on to a more profound understanding of the earth, in particular in the 20th. century, by building on the very perceptive and systematically painstaking work of people like James Hutton.

Having established the general distribution of rocks in the area by systematic mapping and recorded the sequence of deposition of the rocks, it is then possible to start to reconstruct the geological story behind the rocks and to re-create the history of the region through geological time. Before any particular area could be studied in this way it was first necessary to establish the sequence known as the 'Stratigraphic Column'. This was slowly constructed by very careful study of the rocks and, in particular, their contained fossils. This process was undertaken by many geologists throughout a prolonged period, stretching from the early 19th Century to the present day, although in practice the main facts have been known for well over half a century. It is the very fine detail that is now the preoccupation of stratigraphers and they are forever re-interpreting rocks to refine their relationships, always with the view to establishing the geological time that they represent, without which any true history is impossible. A simple stratigraphic column is included to give you the main features and the ages of the different periods of time (Fig. 1). But time is an elusive part of the story of any rock and its true age, as measured in years, is not at all easy to establish, so how do we find out about time?

Whilst it is undoubtedly interesting to know something about the actual numbers of years that elapsed between various episodes, I doubt if many readers will be able to envisage what a million years could be like and this is the basic unit of time to a geologist, anything less seems to be rather trivial! So whilst it is fascinating to think that a fossil that you pick up could easily be 200 million years old, there could easily be another nearby that is 300 million years old and there are certainly some rare ones from the region that are at least 400 million years old. These enormous figures usually impress people and if you want a good put-down you could try them on your friends next time they show you a newly acquired antique. In fact they are mere chickens compared with the age of many rocks and numbers seem rather meaningless when they get this big.

Geological time is no different from any other sort, of course. There is simply a lot of it. The standard unit of time, effectively one million years, is often represented in books and diagrams as Ma. As mentioned above, this is not a period which any human can relate to so we might as well not worry about it excepting for one very fundamental and important aspect. To do justice to the real length of time involved in rocks you have to adjust your normal way of judging events in terms of their probability. To give an example; nobody in their right mind who knew nothing of geological time would concede that it is possible that Britain and America were once joined together and subsequently split apart. This split has in fact happened but how do we know? We can actually see this happening in Iceland and if you had a submarine you could also observe it all along the centre of the Atlantic Ocean. By an extremely slow and gradual process that is still going on today the two continents were separated by the creation of the rocks of the bed of the Atlantic Ocean. The speed of spreading is extremely slow, although it is perfectly easy to see in a few years. A typical rate of movement is about two or three centimetres per year.

Most intelligent people might find it unremarkable to observe an earth movement of two or three centimetres, after all it is not uncommon to see such movements in house foundations and other large structures. But how many would make the intellectual leap to realise that the Atlantic Ocean itself was created by such modest movements added up over millions of years? It takes a new and broader way of thinking to explain everyday phenomena seen in geology, perhaps like that of the famous 'fool on the hill' of the Beatles' song who watched the sun sinking and saw the Earth spinning round. In geological time the almost unthinkable becomes possible. I will even go further and argue that not only is the unthinkable possible, given enough time it almost becomes inevitable! Let me try to explain what I mean. We all of us tend to assume that rare events will never happen to us. What would you say were your chances of being struck by a meteorite in your lifetime? Probably you would stab a guess at it and let us suppose that you say 'One in a million'. This rather loose guess effectively means 'None at all'. If the chance was in fact one in a million and you stood around for a million lifetimes, i.e. about 90 million years (let's be generous) you would quite probably be struck by a meteorite. If you hung around for two or three such periods, let's say around 270 million years, you would run a high risk of being hit (a 3:1 on chance isn't it?) and now the 'impossible' has become the worryingly likely. Naturally enough, none of us is

Fig 2: The map of the whole county shows the major stratigraphical units, each representing rocks which were deposited during one geological Period. This map was drawn using British Geological Survey maps at 1:250,000, Sheets 50N 04W and 51N 04W.

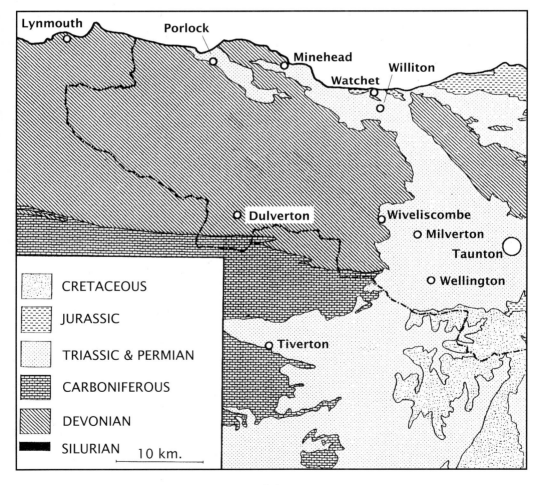

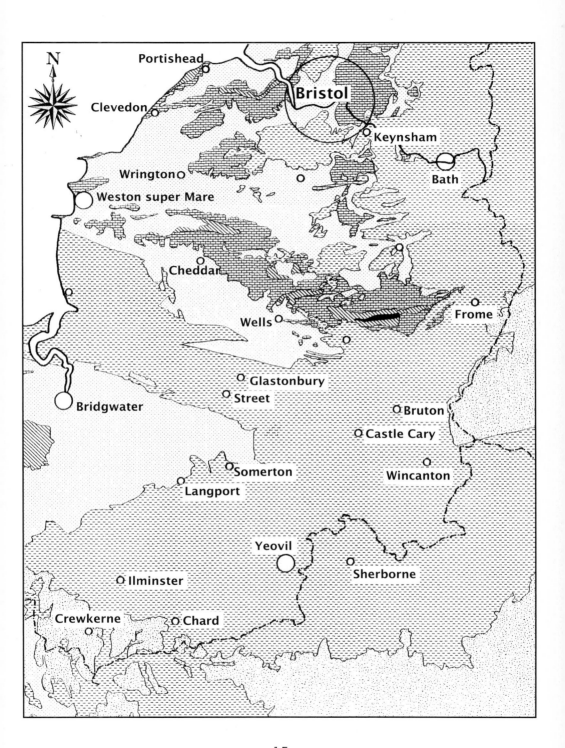

going to be troubled by such odds but the earth has been around for a lot longer than 270 million years, more like 4,600 million in fact. What chance of any one place on the Earth's surface being hit by a meteorite now? It has gone from being highly improbable to almost an absolute certainty. So, to move on to things real, we live rather blinkered lives in which little seems to change, but if you watch long enough you can actually see the processes working that drove the earth to its present state. In this way it is not so difficult to believe in some of the rather preposterous sounding claims of geologists; for example, that the continents were once joined together in one super-continent rather than being scattered over the globe as they are now. Or that Somerset, which now rests in the cool-temperate part of the northern hemisphere was once, not so very long ago geologically speaking, well south of the Equator and has drifted northwards to its present position over the last four hundred million years.

So to understand geology we need to be prepared to consider almost anything possible and to open our minds to the environments of the entire world. Here in Somerset there have been hot deserts, tropical rain-forests, shallow coral seas, and even volcanoes! In case you find this hard to believe let me point out that even within our lifetimes the weather patterns have clearly changed and at the close of the 20th Century we appear to be entering a period of rather milder conditions, with fewer cold winters and hotter summers. It was only about two hundred years ago that the rivers used to freeze up regularly in winter, whereas now we rarely see such things. If such changes can occur in a few hundred years, or perhaps even in decades, how much more might be possible in millions of years?

Somerset is a county with diverse geology but none of its rocks dates back more than around 430 million years, i.e. to within the last tenth of the history of the earth as a whole. In Britain the oldest rocks that we have (in northern Scotland) are probably around 2,800 million years old and there are plenty of rocks 500-1000 million years old, so in Somerset we are only going to be studying the latter parts of the history of the earth. Even so we shall see evidence for dramatic changes in climate and environment, the evolution of most of our modern life-forms and the loss of others, as well as tracing the stages in the formation of the county from its earliest beginnings).

The distribution of the rocks in Somerset is seen in the maps which show the outcrops of the major rock units (Fig. 2. Given a map of the county and knowing the stratigraphic sequence of its rocks, where should we actually start our study? The very oldest rocks that outcrop in the county are of mid-Silurian age, around 427 million years old and are volcanic lavas and ashes. They occur in the Moons Hill quarry on the Mendip Hills, close to Stoke St. Michael. However, their exposure is very limited and they have no significant impact on the scenery of the region. The oldest rocks that we see in any quantity are those of the Devonian Period which are mostly sedimentary rocks with a range of sandstones, grits and fine-grained muds. Some of these are now converted to slates. There are occasional limestones, especially in the Quantock area. The majority of these Devonian rocks are seen in the west of the county, e.g. around Minehead, Porlock and south to Dulverton. There are also plenty of good exposures in the Quantock Hills near Taunton. Further north the coastal sections around Clevedon and Portishead offer excellent material for study. Wherever you go to look at these rocks you will find a similarity in the majority of exposures, that is the rocks are sandy, muddy or gritty, with large pebble conglomerates in places. Only in the west of the county will you see limestones however, since these were not deposited further north. There are even some minor areas of Devonian rocks high up on the Mendip Hills where they are surrounded by large expanses of later Carboniferous limestones.

The Carboniferous system was the one that followed the Devonian, starting at around 360 million years ago, and is well exposed in Somerset in the Mendip Hills. We have a reasonably complete sequence in Somerset and many of the major units are present. Rocks of this age are best known in Britain from the Pennines, Wales, Scotland and Ireland. The characteristic rock of the system is a pure white or grey limestone. This is very hard, having been cemented together since it was first deposited from shallow tropical seas as a soft white ooze, and contains fossils of many kinds including corals and shells which might have lived in shallow lagoons. As well as the lower Carboniferous limestones which produce the high ground of the Mendip Hills you will find the younger Coal Measures here too, although exposures are rarer. This is simply because these younger rocks are easily weathered and have been buried by vegetation and soil. The Coal Measure rocks are largely those of estuarine conditions in which muds and sands were alternately inter-bedded with plant debris which eventually became modified by heat and pressure into coal. This sequence of coal, mudstone and sandstone gives the typical rhythmic layering which is a characteristic feature of the Coal Measures. The Coal Measures were the source of the valuable seams of coal on which the area once depended for its fuel and formed the basis of the industrialisation of the northern part of the county in the 19th century. The remains of old coal mines are now well hidden by vegetation but there are still a number of sites where you can see the volcano-like heaps of shale which was dumped as waste by the miners of old. Some of these tips have been re-worked in latter years to remove the considerable quantities of waste coal that was in them, and subsequent 'landscaping' of the sites has effectively destroyed this last vestige of the former industry.

The Coal Measures are often covered by a thin veneer of younger rocks. These are generally very easy to locate because the soil that results from weathering the earliest of them, the New Red Sandstone of the Triassic, is very obviously red in colour and friable and light. This gives the ploughed fields of the Vale of Taunton Deane and the western areas of the county a very pleasing mellow brick-red colour in spring and autumn, and some of their exposures, as in the cliffs of the coast around the northern Quantocks, are spectacularly bright. This colour is found widely throughout the county and is indicative of this most important transition from Palaeozoic rocks to the Mesozoic ones. This happened about 250 million years ago and in the west of the county there are some of the older beds of the Triassic, with coarse pebble conglomerates and sandstones around the Milverton area. In the central and northern parts of the county the rocks are usually soft fine-grained sands and silts and these give low ground with deep red soils.

Following the red sediments we find pale cream or grey limestones of the Rhaetic, about 200 million years old. As we move upwards these first marine sediments of the Mesozoic become increasingly dark grey shales and limestones of the lower Lias, the first unit of the Jurassic. These have the distinguishing definitive feature of containing the first British ammonites. These fossils can easily be found wherever the rocks are exposed, from the coast near Watchet in the west to the central Somerset levels around Street and occasionally further north around the Mendips and towards Bath. The Jurassic system is the main unit which occupies the centre and east of the county and most of the rocks from these areas are from some part of it.

In general, you will find that the further south and east you are in Somerset the younger are the rocks. This is simply due to the fact that all of these Mesozoic strata are gently inclined to the east at a few degrees from the horizontal. There are steeper dips locally, caused by folding movements, but the general dip is less than ten degrees and results in a fairly flat plateau-like topography with slight escarpments, or steps, leading upwards for a few metres to the next wide dip slope. Excellent examples of this sort of feature can be seen in central Somerset around Ilminster where a thin limestone known as the Junction Bed forms a fairly resistant edge to some plateau-like features which, incidentally, are strewn with abundant ammonites and other fossils.

The latest part of the story of the geology of Somerset misses out quite a big chunk of geological time. The latest Jurassic rocks are covered by rocks of the Cretaceous sequence but the earliest part of this, dating back to around 135 million years, is missing. Apparently it was never deposited this far west because the area was uplifted above sea level at the close of the Jurassic and missed out on the first inundation of the returning sea. Thus there are no lower Cretaceous rocks in Somerset. An even greater gap in the rock record occurs after this.

When the Cretaceous system finished, at around 65 million years ago, the whole region dried out and the newly created land rose, again in the west, leaving only the eastern corner of southern England under the water and then only for part of the time. During this period the Somerset area was dry land until erosion reduced its level down almost to that of the sea. This process took many millions of years and there are no sediments dating back further than the Pleistocene period, which is only about 2 million years old. Elsewhere in western Britain there is clear evidence of earlier marine deposits than this and it seems probable that Somerset was covered by the sea, but no trace survives locally to reliably prove it. After prolonged erosion the county finally became more or less as we see it today, with the Somerset levels just below sea level. Occasional disturbances lifted them to expose the marine deposits. Were it not for sea-defences and constant pumping in recent years, we should lose quite an area of Somerset back to the sea, or at least to swamps and marshes.

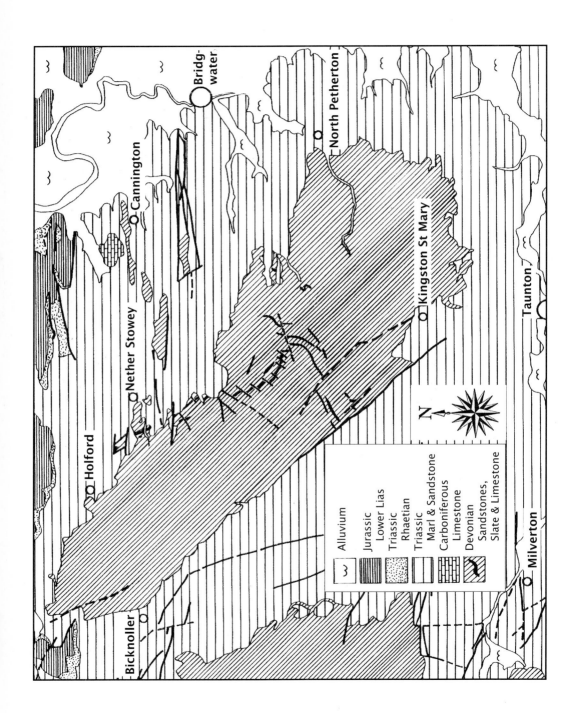

Bridg-water

North Petherton

Cannington

Kingston St Mary

Nether Stowey

Taunton

Holford

N

Bicknoller

Milverton

Alluvium

Jurassic
Lower Lias

Triassic
Rhaetian

Triassic
Marl & Sandstone

Carboniferous
Limestone

Devonian
Sandstones,
Slate & Limestone

The Quantocks,
Brendons and Exmoor

Landscape features

This vast area of western Somerset is relatively underpopulated, since much of it is at very high altitude and is as yet poorly cultivated due to the harsh climatic conditions, the acid soils on the peat moors and the poor drainage . It is split into two by the broad valley of Taunton Deane which extends from Taunton to the coast at Watchet. Thus the Quantock Hills are separated from the rest of the region but otherwise the geological continuity is unbroken, not only within the county, but far beyond into north Devon too (Fig. 4). Many places on the eastern side of Exmoor rise well above 300-400 metres and Dunkery Beacon, at over 500 metres above sea level is easily the highest place in Somerset. The highest parts of the Brendons and the Quantocks are above 300 metres (Fig. 5) but the general level falls as we move further east into the county of Somerset and the eastern end of the Quantocks disappears gently into the Somerset plain. Thus, the whole region could be seen as an inclined slab of rocks, dipping slightly to the east, which has been divided by faults and dissected by rivers. This simplicity is illusory however, because these rocks are actually highly folded and faulted and are now exposed due to the removal of considerable amounts, not only of them, but also of overlying layers. We see today the eroded surface of a block of rocks which has been deformed, buried and re-exposed, and it is this ancient basement which is the foundation of the scenery.

Structural controls on the topography

The break between the Quantocks and the remaining region to the west is a very significant one geologically because it is caused in part by an anticlinal fold and also by a fault of considerable magnitude which has cut through this region. Together they have elevated the south-western side of the Quantocks

Opposite, Fig 3: The main geological units and major faults around the Quantock Hills are shown in this diagram. Devonian rocks occupy all of the high ground to the west, beyond the edge of this map, and details of the lower ground appear in the map accompanying the Chapter on the Somerset coast. (Drawn from BGS Sheet 295)

above the general level of the valley, allowing younger rocks to be deposited in the area to the west of the hills (Fig. 6). The road from Taunton to Williton (the A358) runs parallel to this fault near Taunton, and although you cannot actually see the fault, the height of the hills to the east is impressive enough to give some idea of its effect (fig. 7). In fact, the true scale of this particular fault is very much greater, even than this, because the effect of its movement is not so much a vertical dislocation of the rocks as a lateral slipping, which resulted in the rocks on the eastern side sliding south-eastwards relative to those on the west. This is made more apparent when we look at the rocks on either side of the valley, and discover that those around Stogumber (in the north-west of the valley), are not so much related to those opposite at Crowcombe, as to those further south around Kingston St. Mary. Such lateral movements in faults is usually found to be on a grand scale and although in this example the movement may only be a few kilometres, it is not the only fault of this type in the region. In fact there are several others cutting through south-west England which together produce a very considerable 'offset' in the rocks. They could be said to have altered the shape of the country, since they result in the mass of north Devon being displaced to the north-west, and thus cause the coastline to project northwards into the Bristol Channel, instead of running down smoothly to the south-west. The Quantock Hills thus preserve a little evidence for a very important structural feature in the fundamental geology of the west of England which has had its effect on all of the landscape.

Rocks of west Somerset

The rocks of this area are of Devonian age and are the oldest to be found in the county, with the exception of the rather minor outcrops of Silurian volcanics in the Mendip Hills. They are almost entirely sedimentary, of various types, but mainly clastic, i.e. composed principally of small particles of solid silicate minerals. These particles were derived from the weathering of parent rocks on a pre-Devonian continental land-mass. Amongst them there are abundant sandstones and also thick sequences of shales, now converted to slates in some cases. There are also minor amounts of limestone interbedded in the sequence. There is even one isolated bed of volcanic ash, known as tuff, and a minor intrusion of igneous rock. The latter is exposed in the grounds of Hestercombe House, near Taunton. Since some of the sediments are slightly metamorphosed it could truly be said that in these rocks, all of which are from the Devonian period, we have examples of all the major types of rock, i.e. igneous, sedimentary and metamorphic. The sequence in which these occur is rather difficult to untangle in the field because, for all their diversity, there are very few beds which contain any recognisable fossils and consequently it is very difficult to

Above, Fig. 4: This view across the Brendon Hills shows the high ground under which Devonian sediments occur.

Below, Fig. 5: The distant Quantock Hills are here seen from the heights of the Brendon Hills at Luxborough. Both are composed of Devonian sediments.

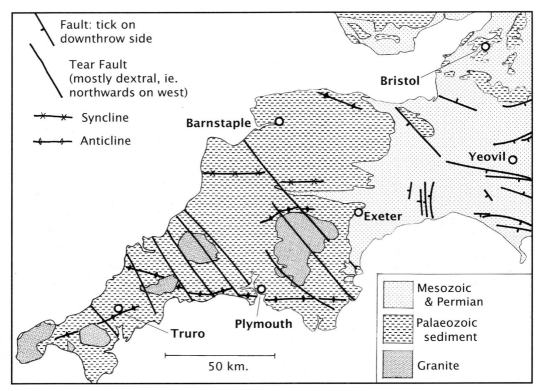

Fig. 6: The south-west of England is cut through by many tear-faults, (also called wrench faults), which trend approximately north-west to south-east. These displace the land to the north-west on their western side, a movement known as 'dextral', and the movement on individual faults can be many kilometres long. Note the displacement of the Permian rocks, showing not only the distance moved, but also that the movement was later than the Permian.

Above, Fig. 7: The south-western face of the Quantock Hills is a fault bounded escarpment which forms a high ridge, with Triassic rocks below the Devonian ones.

Below, Fig. 8: Devonian limestone from Doddington, at the northern end of the Quantock Hills includes crinoid debris and corals, (*Thamnopora cervicornis*)

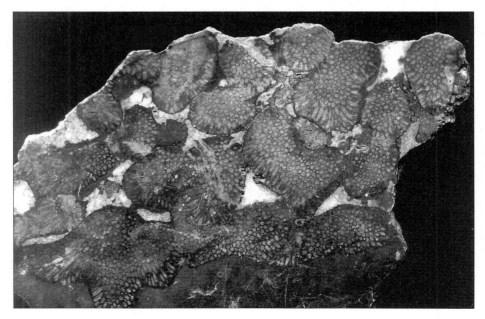

Above, Fig. 9: Devonian limestone from Doddington at the northern end of the Quantock Hills includes crinoid debris. *Below, Fig. 10:* The cave at Holwell on the Quantock Hills is formed in one of the thin limestone bands of Devonian age.

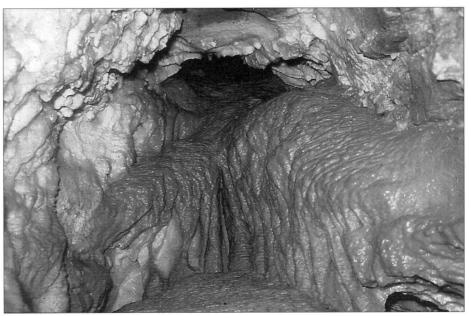

Above, Fig. 11: On the roof of Holwell cave are curiously shaped crystalline masses of the Calcium carbonate mineral Aragonite.

Below, Fig. 12: Triscombe Quarry on the Quantock Hills worked the Devonian sandstones.

Above, Fig. 13: The Devonian sandstones of the Quantock Hills exposed at a road cutting.

Below, Fig. 14: Doddington copper mine is now remembered by the presence of this old engine house. The former counting house of the mine is still visible on the main road from where this picture was taken.

reliably relate outcrops which are separated by any distance from one another.

The latest geological map of the region (sheet 295 of the Taunton area at 1:50,000) does show the stratigraphy in some detail and it is a useful companion to have with you on geological outings, as are the other maps of the county, of course. The absence of fossils is fortunately not universal, otherwise it would be a rather dull sequence of sediments, since they do not exhibit tremendous variety. There are some very well preserved fossil corals and crinoids found on the Quantocks (Fig. 8). These are readily identifiable as belonging to the Devonian period and are found in the red-stained limestones which were formerly quarried along the north-eastern flank of the hills. There are few accessible localities now but you might still see specimens of the rock in local walls and buildings. It is, I hope, needless to say that they should be left there!

Apart from these few corals, there are very few other fossils that you might expect to find in the rocks of this period, at least from this area, although in the region around Portishead, close to Bristol, there are some rather exciting finds recorded. Why should it be that a thick sequence of rocks is so devoid of life? There is of course a good reason and it is simply that the rocks were deposited in a very hostile environment, in a desert in fact, and that there were very few animals around at the time. Land plants had barely begun to evolve and there would have been nothing for animals to eat on the land. Some of the beds, especially the limestones, were clearly deposited in sea-water and since the climate was warm the seas were apparently suitable for corals to flourish in them. In other examples of water-lain sediments, the water was probably fresh and resulted from run-off after rainstorms, so the chance of animal life colonising these torrential and temporary streams was virtually nil. The majority of these Devonian sediments were apparently laid down on the coastal plains of a continental area that was being supplied with abundant sands and muds by weathering of an inland mountainous region, and since similar rocks are found over most of Britain, it is reasonable to suppose that the area of land was very extensive, indeed of continental scale.

Climate and landscape during the Devonian period

The almost universal red staining seen in these rocks is a sure indicator that they were deposited in a region under the influence of an arid climate. The red stain is caused by the highly oxidised iron mineral, Haematite, and under more normally hydrated conditions this would not form, but the hydroxides of iron would be deposited, giving the sediments a brown or yellow colour. Thus we can be confident that, even though some of the rocks were laid down in water, they resulted from weathering in a predominantly dry climate. These rocks are generally coarse grained, including many sandstones as well as some gravel and pebble beds, and there are also some mud sequences.

The materials for these sediments would originally have been the uplands of some continental land-mass which was elevated before the Devonian period. In fact, it was at the close of the preceding Silurian period, when much of Britain was affected by severe mountain building earth movements. These disturbances are known as the Caledonian Orogeny, since they largely affect northern Britain. The effect of these movements was to close an ocean basin which had been in existence for hundreds of millions of years, in a position more or less comparable with that of the Atlantic today. As the two sides of the ocean were brought together by the gradual movement of the earth's plates, the continental masses on each side forced the sea floor sediments up into piles which became elevated into mountains. There are still remnants of these in northern Britain and throughout the line of collision, including the eastern side of north America and western Scandinavia. These Caledonian mountains were the source of a great amount of sediment, as they weathered away in the dry climate of the Devonian period, and their remains are preserved in sedimentary deposits of various types, depending upon the local conditions.

Thus, we can expect to find beds of rock which represent all the varied features of a desert landscape today, e.g. there may be screes on the flanks of hills. There should be river valleys and flood plains, dried up lakes and shorelines, desert sand-dunes and wind-blown dust deposits. In the rocks of the Devonian period in Britain, all of these are indeed found, and in this area of Somerset we can see examples of some of them. In particular, we find sands and muds well represented. This suggests that in this area we were well removed from the primary site of weathering and received mainly the finer grained materials, excepting during flood conditions when coarser pebbles were washed in by the temporarily swollen rivers.

Places to visit

Although the Devonian rocks are very widespread throughout western Somerset, they are not especially well exposed in many convenient places. They have been used in the past for building stones, including the roofing slates of the Brendon Hills, and there are many old quarries in the region of the Devon borders south of Wiveliscombe, some of which are accessible, albeit rather overgrown. There are also some old limestone quarries on the Quantocks which may yield occasional fossil corals and there is a small cave system developed in the limestones at Holwell (Figs. 10 & 11). Roadside cuttings and quarries are available and some of these are well situated. There is a quarry on the top of North Hill, above Porlock, but approached from Minehead, which is well worth the long drive just for the views, as much as the geological interest. The very large quarry at Triscombe (Fig 12) and other smaller ones on the Quantocks are also useful exposures, usually in the harder sandstones. In addition to the old quarries there are many places where road improvements have cut through the Devonian rocks and if they have not been covered by soil or seeded they should remain visible for at least a few years. There is one especially clear section through mixed sandstones and muds on the main Bridgwater to Minehead road near St. Audries. On this section you can see how the dip of the beds varies as you follow the bend in the road, a useful example of how apparent dip is not always the true one (Fig. 13)! But I would urge you not to stop to look at this one since the road is so busy, and your presence as a pedestrian would be potentially very dangerous to yourself and to drivers. Choose a quieter road with wider verges, park well off the road, and you can enjoy a close examination in peace.

The Quantocks were once a source of small amounts of copper and the old mine at Doddington is still remembered by the engine house, standing close to the road from Bridgwater to Minehead (Fig. 14). The mine 'Counting House' is still visible on the road close to the engine house.

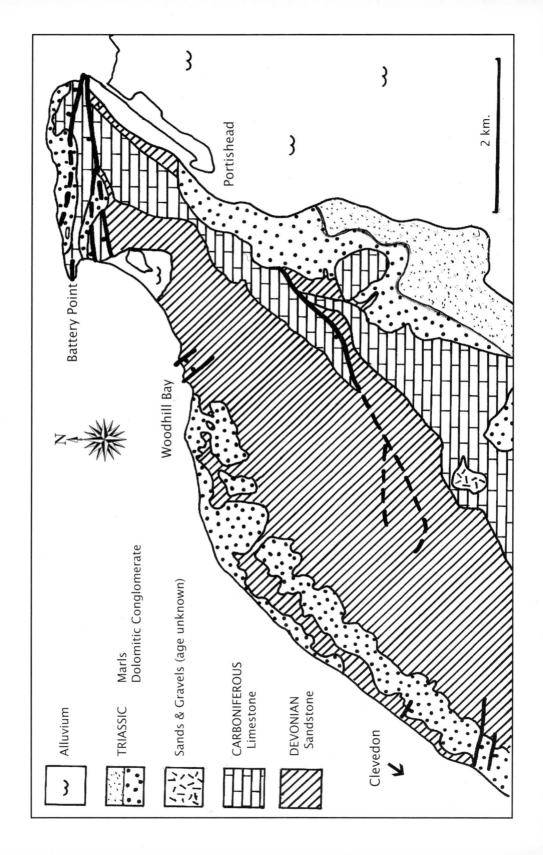

Alluvium

TRIASSIC
  Marls
  Dolomitic Conglomerate

Sands & Gravels (age unknown)

CARBONIFEROUS
  Limestone

DEVONIAN
  Sandstone

N

2 km.

Battery Point

Portishead

Woodhill Bay

Clevedon

The Portishead to Clevedon Coast

The northern part of the county is a wedge-shaped piece of land, lying between the Severn estuary and the Mendip Hills, with its northern boundary at the River Avon. It includes the high ground of the Failand Ridge, which stretches from Clevedon at its southwestern end to Portishead at the northeastern end, a distance of about six miles. This ridge protects the Gordano valley from the erosive efforts of the River Severn, and is formed from the highly resistant Devonian sandstone and Carboniferous limestones, similar to the rocks seen in the Mendip Hills, just a few miles to the south.

From its crest there are dramatic views in all directions and as a starting point from which to spy out the land it is hard to better. To the north there are uninterrupted views up the River Severn, on a clear day as far as the Malvern Hills, whilst to the west there is a panorama of the Forest of Dean and south Wales. On the southern shore of the Bristol Channel, the steep cliff of North Hill at Minehead is sometimes plain, with the high ground of the Brendon Hills and Exmoor rising behind to Dunkery Beacon. Further to the south are the flat-topped Blackdown Hills with the Quantock Hills between them and the estuary, lying just north of Taunton, the County Town. Further round to the south east are the low lying levels and the Mendip Hills rise close by, obscuring most of the view from there to the east. In the estuary can be seen the headlands at Weston-super-Mare; Sand Point in the north, Worlebury Hill at Weston itself, and further round to the south is Brean Down. Out in the estuary are the conspicuous islands of Steep and Flat Holm, and you won't have any trouble working out which is which!

You will also notice, unavoidably I am afraid, the noise of the traffic on the M5, which cuts its way through the hill above the narrow Clevedon Gap at the southern end of the valley. This gap is the point at which the ridge on which you stand is faulted away from the further one, along the side of which the motorway has been cut. So steep are the faulted sides of that hill that the carriageway has been split into two levels for part of its length. This, the Clevedon fault, repeats the geology on both ridges. It is the sediments to the

---

Opposite, Fig. 15: The ridge that extends from Portishead to Clevedon is largely composed of Devonian and Carboniferous rocks, surrounded by Triassic conglomerate. (Taken from BGS Sheet 264).

west of the Failand Ridge which are of especial interest, because these are rather older than most others seen in Somerset, and are far better exposed than many because they outcrop on the rocky shores around Portishead and Clevedon. The easier location to see them at is Portishead, so let's go there and start off on the sea-front.

The best place to start is probably about one hundred metres south of the headland where the swimming pool is, and here the beach is quite clean and often dry, so it is an easy matter to step through a gap in the bank between the road and the beach, and there you are, straight into some very interesting geology. On the beach you will find some small ridges of solid rock poking up through the pebbles and running more or less straight out to sea. These are worth a close look. They are composed of thin beds of hard limestone, and are interesting because they are so tightly folded (Fig. 16). The folds cause the beds to arch upwards and to be depressed into troughs and they are only a matter of a few metres across, so the change in attitude of the beds is very rapid. You can wander along a few tens of metres and see the folds repeating, and clearly the strata on this section are quite highly contorted. As you get closer to the headland at the north eastern end of the beach you should look around in the loose rocks for signs of fossils. They are here, and you might be lucky and find a trilobite, I once did! If you don't see one, then I am sure that you will find many other fossils to compensate you, and a search of the cliffs nearby will certainly reveal shells of one sort or another, especially brachiopods and crinoids.

If you carry on to the headland and look on the northern side, you will find an interesting exposure about 50 metres east of the small navigation beacon where the rocks display some erosional features. The lowest rocks are apparently steeply dipping beds of Carboniferous limestones, similar to those that you saw on your way from the beach, but overlying them there are boulders and less steeply dipping beds of rock, which represent the basal layers of the younger Triassic period. These coarse conglomerates mark the end of a long period of erosion, during which the Carboniferous deposits were cut down and broken up into boulders, pebbles and sand, and the debris from the last stages of this process is still lying around on the eroded surface to remind us of this event. Nearby, there are other near-horizontal cracks in the lower set of rocks. These cracks are fault planes, and were formed during the episode of elevation which up-ended the Lower Carboniferous sediments to form the ridges of the Mendip Hills and this isolated northern ridge. These earth movements were very severe and caused enormous slabs of rock to be moved relative to one another along these fault planes. On this headland you can see the polished surfaces of one of these faults which cuts through the rocky shoreline and leaves a smooth platform on the otherwise irregular surface. Not all of the faults are horizontal, indeed some are nearly vertical, but they add up to a complex of fractures which together demonstrate substantial movements of the crust of the earth (Fig. 17).

The real purpose of this excursion is not to look at Carboniferous features however, but to examine the red rocks which are exposed at the southern end of this bay, so you now need to retrace your steps and walk back towards the boating pool, and beyond, taking to the beach in the centre of the bay, and following the sea-wall until you get to its end. When you reach the shore beyond the sea-wall don't hurry, but look carefully at the cliffs on your left (Fig. 18). You should see a very conspicuous rock face with very well displayed strata of sandstone, and lots of white pebbles of Quartz gleaming in the rock. These pebbles are the remnants of seams of Quartz that once penetrated through ancient hills, now totally destroyed by erosion, and redistributed as gravels which were laid down and buried as long ago as the Devonian period, about 360-410 million years ago. These rocks are variously tinted, from buff or grey to brick red, individual bands are more or less red depending largely upon how they have weathered. The best colour is generally seen in the finer grained silts and muds which also occur in this section on the shore, and which can be seen in undercuts in the low cliffs. The reason why these fine-grained silts have retained their red colour so well is probably because they are constantly eroding away, being quite soft, and so are refreshed and still show their proper colour, whereas the sands are much harder and slower to erode and so lose their colour to slow solution of the iron oxide by the rain. Incidentally, whilst on the subject of cliffs, you are wearing your hard-hat aren't you? I know you feel stupid with it on, when anyone else on the beach is either sunbathing or walking safely a few yards from the cliffs, but even a small rock landing on your head from a height of a few metres will make your eyes water, and persuade you to wear it next time, if there is one!

Now, back to that red colour. You will now know, if you have read the chapter on the vale of Taunton Deane or Watchet area, that red means oxidised iron and arid conditions of deposition. You will also consequently realise that these rocks are the result of deposition from an arid climate. However, it is also reasonable to suppose that the Quartz pebbles that they contain are the result of water erosion and transport, it is hardly likely that they were wind-blown, so there must have been water about. In fact, there certainly was, but not all the time. In any desert there will occasionally be rainstorms and these are often dramatic, with serious flash flooding following the run-off which a lack of vegetation causes. Thus, in typical deserts, the coarsest sediments are transported very rapidly during floods and are deposited as course-grained sands and gravels, with muds and silts settling out in the quieter periods. If you look again at these silty beds in the cliff, you should find places where they are cut through by the overlying sands and gravels, and in these overlying beds you may see

Above, Fig. 16: The limestones and shales of the lower Carboniferous close to Battery Point at Portishead are crumpled into tight folds by compression from the south.

Below, Fig. 17: At Battery Point, Portishead, the Carboniferous limestone exhibits faults at shallow angles of dip which were caused by thrust movements from the south.

Above, Fig. 18: The cliffs at Kilkenny Bay, just south from the sea-front at Portis-head, display sandstones and other sediments of Devonian and Triassic age.
Below, Fig. 19: The strong currents which transported the sand and gravel to make this sedimentary bed also tore up previously deposited muds, which became trapped as soft pellets and subsequently weathered out of the rock, leaving voids.

flakes of the mud trapped in the gravel. This demonstrates that the muds were sometimes only temporary deposits, and that some of them were removed by erosion when the next flood occurred, whilst others were preserved by rapid burial by yet more sands (Fig. 19).

Clearly, these deposits represent a very turbulent environment, and they are the result of the rapid uplift of the land above sea-level, and its subsequent erosion, at the beginning of Devonian times. The first formed sediments were gravels and sands and they were only transported for relatively short distances during times of flood, after which they lay around in the dried-up river beds where they were undisturbed until the next episode of flooding. If you now look a little further along the shore, maybe a few hundred metres along from the sea-wall end, you will start to find evidence that some of the later rocks were so vigorously deposited that they cut across the earlier ones and removed them. You will find places where there are cross-cutting gravels and very large pebbles, and even boulders, resting upon an eroded surface, with the older rocks underneath truncated by the upper ones.

This is an example of an unconformity and is a classic one at that. The two rock units look very similar. They are both made up of sands and gravels, both contain pebbles of Quartz and are stained red by iron. The only difference is that the lower one is Devonian in age, and the upper one is Triassic, and there is a gap of about 100 million years between them! During that time gap the Carboniferous Limestones of the Mendip Hills were laid down, as were the Coal Measures that followed them, and Britain drifted across the surface of the planet from a position south of the Equator to one north of it. This remarkable break in the geological record demonstrates just how much erosion must have gone on here in the past because it is only a few hundred metres away that we can see the Carboniferous rocks exposed, and yet here they are entirely missing.

We can also determine that this erosion must have commenced very swiftly on completion of the deposition of the Carboniferous rocks because the Triassic deposits followed it, a mere forty million years later. This period of erosion, the Permian, is not represented in the sediments at Portishead and the oldest beds we see are the basal gravels and pebble beds of the lower Triassic. These are probably synchronous with extensive pebble beds from the basal Triassic at Milverton in west Somerset, which are equivalent to the Budleigh Salterton Pebble Beds of Devon, and represent the remains of rocks which also were being eroded during the Permian times. Thus, we see here evidence for a tremendous Permian upheaval, known as the Variscan, Hercynian or Armorican orogeny, which marked the end of the Palaeozoic era and the beginning of the new order of things in the Mesozoic, which commenced with the Triassic (Fig. 20).

Most of the Quartz pebbles that we see in the Portishead rocks are not from the Mendip Hills but were probably derived from further away, outside the region. How can we tell where the pebbles come from? Well, if you look again at those cliff sections, or at any of the better displayed sets of beds on the shore, you will see that the bedding in them is not horizontal but regularly slopes at an angle, mostly in one predominant direction. This direction alters from bed to bed, but in each case it tells you which way the current was flowing as that bed was being laid down. In brief, the downward slope faces downstream, so it faces in the direction of the current. If you measure enough of these current directions you build up a picture of the general trends and with this information you can begin to tell where the sediment was derived from. Repeat the exercise elsewhere and you get a picture of the region as a whole and from this you can start to reconstruct the map of ancient 'Britain'. Try it here, and see which direction *you* think most of the beds suggest as the source for the current (Fig. 21).

Having established the broad picture of the geology of this section, you can now indulge yourself in a bit of fossil hunting if you wish. There are some very unusual ones recorded from here and amongst them there are plenty of small bones and scales of some quite large fish. One, called *Holoptychius*, had scales that were roughly rounded and about the size of an old penny. If you don't remember them, they were circa 3cms in diameter! The scales and bones are often found mixed up with mud flakes in the coarser gravel beds, but the best preserved might be found in the finer silts of the famous Woodhill Bay Fish Bed, which is a ten metre thick unit of finer grained sediments found part way along the beach. The fish remains are usually much paler coloured than the rest of the sediment, often a shade of white, tinged milky blue, and the bones are also rather porous and spongy in sections, so you can distinguish them from ordinary pebbles quite easily. These fish remains are typical of the Devonian period in Britain and represent the origins of vertebrate life in this county.

The earliest forms were heavily armoured fish-like creatures called Agnathans which had no true jaws, but after a major break in the Devonian period, represented in this section by a change in the sedimentary sequence from muds to sandstones, the later forms, including *Holoptychius*, were true fishes with jaws and proper scales. There were older animals with backbones in the Silurian period but they were very small and scarce, so the evolution of the Devonian fishes was the onset of higher animal life in many places. The fossils are now found in what are presumed to be flash flood deposits of a river, so it seems likely that the 'fish' were living in fresh water, rather than the sea, and that they occupied an otherwise rather hostile environment of arid climate in which there was very little terrestrial life of any sort, plant or animal. It was during this Devonian period that the first tiny land plants began to evolve but it is unlikely

Above, Fig. 20: The Triassic conglomerates rest directly upon the Devonian rocks at Kilkenny Bay, all of the Carboniferous rocks having first been removed by deep erosion. *Below, Fig. 21:* The sandstones at Kilkenny Bay are cross-bedded due to the transport of the sand in strong currents. The sloping surfaces are the downstream sides of what were once ripple fronts.

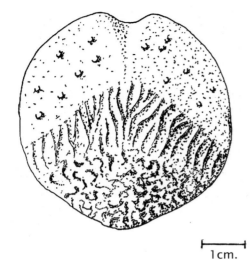

Left, Fig. 22: The few fossils found in Devonian sands and muds include a large fish, *Holoptychius*, which had roughly circular scales bearing strong ornament.

├───────┤
1cm.

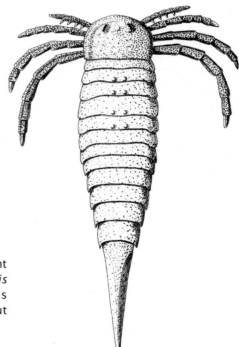

Right, Fig. 23: Finds in 1947 of the giant arthropod *Drepanopterus abonensis* associated with *Holoptychius* scales show that there were scavengers about to clear up any dead fish.

41

Above, Fig. 24: Cornstone is a mixture of sands and gravels with a cement which replaces some of the earlier sand, leaving the remainder suspended between lime nodules.

that there were any large land animals in this area (Fig. 22).

The fish in the rivers probably ate aquatic animals, such as molluscs or arthropods. We have little evidence for this but we do know that there were arthropods around in the area because some exceptional fossils that have been found here are indeed arthropods, but of an amazing size. These are the so-called 'Sea-scorpions', a wonderfully evocative and descriptive name for an animal that appears not to have been a scorpion nor to have lived in the sea! However, they were elongated and had big claw-like limbs at the front end, and they were certainly aquatic, so the name is not entirely outrageous. The one from Portishead is known to have grown to be around half a metre in length but others from elsewhere have been as much as two metres, and these would certainly have been a force to reckon with, especially to fish only ten or twenty centimetres long! This may explain why many of these early fish had such heavily armoured skeletal plates around their heads and why the *Holoptychius* scales are so thick and bony. There were dangerous predators about and a tough armour-plated body made good sense. You can see a model of the beast itself in the City Museum in Bristol, by the way. The molluscan diet that the fish might have enjoyed is not seen in Portishead, unless perhaps you are fortunate enough to be the first to discover it, but at Lydney on the opposite shores of the Severn and only about 25 miles to the north, there are abundant bivalves in the sediments of similar age, and these bivalves could clearly have been living here too (Fig. 23).

Another rather unusual rock occurs on this shore. This is a limestone, which would not normally be expected to be associated with pebbly and sandy sediments, especially when river-borne, as in this case. Limestones are usually associated with open shallow seas, or lagoonal areas in hot climates. We have seen that the climate was arid during the time of the Devonian, when red sediments were deposited, and it was the dry climate which caused water which was trapped in the ground to be evaporated and as it dried up it left behind any salts that had been dissolved in it. In this area the salt that was left behind was Calcium carbonate and this filled up the pore spaces in the sediment between the grains of sand and the pebbles. In practice, the lime actually replaced some of the sand grains and there was a chemical reaction going on in the sediment during the deposition of the lime, but the effect was much the same as if it had simply been deposited in the pores because the lime now occupies the spaces between the residual sand grains. The rock which resulted is curiously lumpy-looking and forms masses which could easily be mistaken for concrete, being pale grey in colour and containing abundant pebbles. I have to confess that on my first visit to this shore I mistook the masses of conglomerate high on the beach for foundations of wartime buildings, imagining the Home Guard settling in to watch for enemy boats trying to sneak in to Bristol! This limestone conglomerate rock is known to geologists as Calcrete but it also has the rather strange name of 'cornstone' which, it has been suggested, is because it was used to make millstones. I cannot confirm this use for the stone however. Calcrete was formed at a time when the sediment supply stopped for a while. During this interval there was time for the ground to dry out and substantial quantities of water were evaporated to produce the solid carbonate deposits. On the Severn shore at Lydney, in the Forest of Dean, there are similar Calcrete deposits which developed into solid limestone horizons and formed hard crusts over the sandstones. These are estimated, by modern analogy, to have taken about 10,000 years to develop fully, so it seems likely that the pause in sedimentation during Devonian times was a substantial one. It is probable that these prolonged periods of dsiccation were times when the river had meandered away from the immediate area, its main channel perhaps being many miles away in a broad river valley. After the channel returned the dehydration was interrupted and the Calcrete formation stopped, to be replaced by more sands and gravels (Fig.24).

The sections along the shore further south from Kilkenny Bay become increasingly difficult of access and it is unnecessary to carry on for more than a few hundred metres. If you wish to go further choose a period when the tide is falling and beware its return, since this area has some of the highest tides in the region and is also facing the worst of the weather!

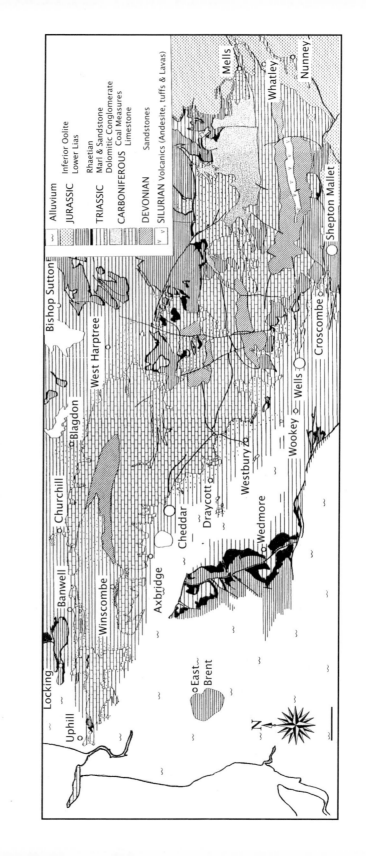

The Mendip Hills

Geographical position

The Mendip Hills rise abruptly from the northern edge of the central Somerset plain and form an unbroken barrier which stretches from the Severn Estuary in the west to the high ground which forms the Somerset borders in the east. The hills reach heights of around 250-300 metres and are the highest land in central Somerset. They are steep-sided, both on the north and south slopes, and this steepness has restricted the number of places suitable for wheeled vehicles to cross so that, even today, there are few roads which cross the hills, especially in the western area. In the east, the Mendip Hills merge with the high ground which extends south from the Cotswolds into the eastern part of Somerset. Here the steep ridges of the hills become an extensive plateau so that the local scenery is less obviously elevated. However, you can still appreciate its height above sea-level because of the depth of the incised valleys which cross this region. There are too many books and articles published about the Mendip Hills to list individually, and there is a Mendip Society for lovers of this relatively wild and scenic part of the county.

Geological Summary

The Mendip Hills owe their origin to a combination of two equally important factors. One of these is the hardness and chemical composition of the rocks from which they are made, which gives them considerable resistance to weathering and erosion. The other is folding and faulting, which originally forced the rocks above the normal ground level to create the hills (Fig. 26). The rocks which form the hills are of two main types, Devonian sandstone and Carboniferous limestone. The sandstone is only seen on the highest ground at the centre of the hills, notably on Blackdown, on North Hill, and also further east near Downhead. The Carboniferous limestones are the most conspicuous rocks of the Mendip Hills and they are found surrounding these older sandstones. They were originally laid down on the sea-bed, over the earlier sandstones,

---

Opposite, Fig. 25: The Mendip Hills extend from their Mesozoic cover around Frome to the shores of the Severn estuary where they form several headlands, Brean Down being the most southerly.
(Map compiled from the British Geological Survey 1:50,000 Sheet 279 and 1:63,360 Sheets 280 and 281).

which they buried to depths of hundreds of metres. Near Downhead a small outcrop of Silurian volcanic ashes and lavas is also found. These igneous rocks are the oldest in Somerset and are located in the core of the fold which forms the central foundation of the hills. They are surrounded by slightly younger Devonian sandstones (Figs. 27 & 28).

Long after the rocks were deposited the area was affected by earth movements which were generated further south and which caused east to west folding in the area. The originally flat-lying rocks were transformed into a series of folds which are now seen in the landscape as ridges. Although individual folds run east to west they are arranged 'en echelon' and lie in a band running west-north-west to east-south-east. The folding resulted firstly in a series of elongate mounds which may originally have risen to heights perhaps twice those of today, but these were eroded away over millions of years to expose the hilltops that we see now. This erosion was caused by weathering processes largely during the Permian and Triassic periods, about 260-210 million years ago, when Britain was positioned close to the equator and had an arid climate.

The sedimentary deposits which resulted from this erosion are usually stained a dull red colour, as a consequence of the arid climate of the time acting upon the iron in the rock, particularly the Iron Pyrites from the Coal Measures, to form a mineral called Haematite. This mineral, and its resulting red stain in the rocks, can be seen in many places on and around the Mendip Hills. Because these Triassic rocks still cover the Mendip limestones in places, we can be certain that the hills as we see them today had already been eroded to their present level long ago in Triassic times. The Mendip Hills are therefore truly ancient, although since their original erosion they have been totally buried by younger rocks and have only emerged in their present form as a result of a more recent phase of weathering and erosion (Fig. 29).

The Jurassic period, which followed the Triassic, was a time when the exposed tops of the Mendip Hills were eroded down to sea level and eventually covered by sea water. After a while marine animals colonised the eroded rock surfaces, sediments gradually buried them, and they were lost from view for millions of years. These younger sediments are still preserved as a thin veneer over the eastern Mendips where they appear as buff-coloured horizontally-layered limestones, lying directly over the grey Carboniferous limestones. At this junction there is often a distinct angular unconformity between the two units of rock. The lower beds are tilted at various angles, whilst the upper ones are resting almost horizontally. The classic section where this can be seen is in Vallis Vale near Frome (Fig. 30). The diagram in Fig. 31 may help to explain this photograph.

Surface indicators of unseen rocks

In the areas where sandstones occur there is a striking change in the natural vegetation. Over much of the Mendip Hills the natural flora is typical of that found on lime soils, with characteristic shrubs such as Spindle (*Euonymous europaeus*) and Wayfaring Tree (*Viburnum lantana*) (Fig. 32). Where the sandstone outcrops, the soil is acid rather than alkaline and a typical flora includes Ling (*Calluna vulgaris*) and Bell Heather (*Erica cinerea*), and in wet places Bilberry (*Vaccinium myrtillus*). These floral differences result in a poor scrubby moorland on the sandstone outcrops with a more shrubby and wooded aspect over the limestone (Fig. 33). As in other areas, an indication of the underlying geology is often gained from studying the stone field-walls. The stone was rarely carried more than a few hundred metres and generally reflects the local geology very closely. Experts in the study of lichens might even be able to tell whether the rock is limestone or not by examining their encrustations, since these too have their preferred substrate.

The rocks of the Mendip Hills

The Silurian Volcanics

These, the oldest rocks in the county, are only exposed in quarries close to the villages of Stoke St. Michael and Downhead, both in the eastern Mendips (Figs. 27 & 28). The volcanic rocks are located in the centre of one of the major folds which brought them to the surface from underneath the cover of younger rocks. They were originally extruded from volcanoes similar to those seen today around the Pacific ocean, which erupted large quantities of ash and lava in explosive outbursts. They represent the same type of volcanic activity that we today associate with the destruction of ocean basins and the creation of new mountain ranges. These rocks are known as Andesites, named after the Andes mountains where they are commonly found. Andesites are usually mid-range in their chemistry between basalts and granitic rocks, and typically are mid-grey or purple colours. The rocks in the Mendips are often purple-brown or greenish colours, the latter being largely due to alteration of some of their minerals to the green mineral, Chlorite. The Silurian volcanics have little impact on the scenery in Somerset due to their restricted outcrop and unfortunately are largely inaccessible except by special arrangement with the quarry owners.

The Old Red Sandstone of the Devonian period

The name of this unit of rock suggests that it should be red in appearance and this is generally true throughout most of Britain, but in the majority of exposures in the Mendips it is not! In practice, most of the surface exposures on Mendip are so well washed by rainwater and leached by weathering that the rocks look a pale grey or buff colour. This may well be superficial though and freshly broken rocks from this period are usually a distinctly purple/red colour, thus justifying their name. The red colour is caused by Haematite, the oxidised iron compound which is commonplace in rocks of this age and reflects their origins in an arid climate. It forms a surface coating on the main constituents of the sediment, i.e. on the grains of Quartz, Feldspar and Mica which make up the sandstones. The Old Red Sandstone was accumulated in a desert environment, usually as sand dunes, or alternatively, in river courses during periods of flooding. The full range of lithologies shows all the normal characteristics of desert deposits. In the Mendips we only see the rocks poorly exposed on the highest moorland in the cores of the main folds such as on Blackdown. They are devoid of lime and, in contrast to the surrounding limestone, give acid soils and a distinctive flora unseen elsewhere on the hills. These Devonian sandstones, named after the area where they were first studied, are described in more detail in the sections on the Quantocks, the Brendons and Exmoor.

The Carboniferous Limestone

The limestones which make the impressive pale grey and white crags of Cheddar gorge are typical of those which form the bulk of the Mendip Hills. They were created over 300 million years ago, during a period of geological time known as the Carboniferous. This name reflects the importance of the abundant seams of Carbon-rich coal found in the rocks from the latter part of this particular period of time. It is also appropriate for these limestones because they too are rich in Carbon, not in the form of coal, but combined with Calcium and Oxygen to form a mineral called Calcite, sometimes referred to as 'Lime'. This term is perhaps more commonly used in the construction industry and amongst farmers for the roasted and 'slaked' mineral, Calcium hydroxide, rather than for Calcite, which is Calcium carbonate. Calcite is one of the most important commercial minerals of modern times and is extracted in enormous quarries, for which the Mendip Hills are justly famous, or infamous, depending upon your point of view. Indeed, quarrying is such a feature of the Mendip Hills that on first approaching the famous Cheddar Gorge from the south, a visitor might be forgiven for mistaking a quarry for the Gorge, since the quarry stands out far more plainly (Fig. 34)! Having found the real Gorge, even more visitors are probably unaware that much of what they see as the grand spectacle of nature is in fact due to Man's influence, in the form of quarrying on the natural cliffs. However, the effect is none the less impressive and weathering has now softened many of the scars.

Varieties of limestone

Driving around the Mendip Hills in a car, you could quickly come to the conclusion that the limestone was rather monotonous and much the same wherever you went. However, this is far from the truth, and careful examination shows that the constituent parts are often distinctly visible and are very variable in their character. It is these small details which make it possible to reconstruct the environment of deposition of the original lime sediment, so it is well worth looking as closely as you can at the rocks, and for this purpose a strong magnifier, such as a hand lens, will be very helpful. One other thing to note is that the surface of the stone is a good place for lichens to live, so be careful that you are not closely studying them, when you thought that you were looking at rock! It can sometimes be quite difficult to be certain what those little lumps and structures under your lens are, so try scratching them with a penknife if you are unsure. Lichens generally are soft and come off easily when you do this to them. The best bits of stone to examine are usually either freshly broken chippings or, better still, weathered pieces that are not yet lichen covered. On the weathered surfaces you will often see the shapes of the lime grains standing out slightly in relief, or picked out in different shades of grey. When you have 'got your eye in' you will be able to distinguish a number of types of limestone.

Muddy limestones

The dullest in appearance are those limestones in which individual grains are simply too small to be seen. These rocks are often very smooth on broken surfaces, looking almost like a piece of cement from a bag which has 'gone off'. This similarity is not entirely coincidental because cement is made from limestone with the addition of a little mud, which together are crushed and roasted. When water is added it sets into a 'stone' not unlike its parent limestone. The mode of origin of these fine-grained rocks is usually attributable to the combined effects of evaporation of sea water, which increases its lime content, and the removal of CO_2 from the water by the photosynthesis of algae. This latter process causes the acidity of the water to be lowered and further reduces the solubility of lime in it. The consequence is that some of the lime can be forced out of solution in the form of microscopic crystals, which then settle out of the water on to the sea-bed. This can be observed to happen in tropical sea water during the heat of the day, when the surface algae cause white patches of lime to form in the waters. If the water is shallow the lime can settle on the sea-bed in a matter of a few hours and will be added to the sediment. If the water is deeper however, the lime cannot always reach the sea-bed before it is once more redissolved as it passes through less alkaline water on its way down (Fig. *35*).

Aragonite and Calcite

The primary precipitate of lime is usually a mineral called Aragonite which is quite distinct from the more usual Calcite found in most of the Carboniferous limestones. Aragonite is not a very stable mineral and with the passage of time it can recrystallise into Calcite. For this reason it is unusual to find any Aragonite in rocks of great age, e.g. over a hundred million years old, and it can only be assumed that it was Aragonite which first formed them. The evidence of another type of fine muddy limestone shows that Aragonite is not always the parent mineral however. This rock is the Chalk, which is ubiquitous in southern England although absent from Somerset. In the Chalk we see a limestone mud which has never recrystallised and is therefore still quite soft and mud-like, (try taking a stroll in a chalk quarry after it has rained if you don't believe me). The reason for this softness is not so much to do with the small size of the original lime grains but is caused by the fact that the original grains were deposited directly as Calcite. As a consequence they could not recrystallise in the way that Aragonite would have done and the rock remains a loose assemblage of mud-sized grains of lime. Without digressing too far into the history of the Chalk, you might like to know that the reason for this difference is that the majority of the tiny grains are fossils, and not inorganic in origin, and that some of these ancient organisms precipitated skeletons of Calcite. So, in these dull-looking muddy limestones of the Mendips we see the true cause for the tough, weather-resisting properties of the Carboniferous Limestone. It is all due to the presence of a strongly cemented matrix of recrystallised mud grains which holds together the rest of the rock, whatever its other constituents may be.

Shelly limestones

The limestones which you will most often encounter will show some grains of lime which are visible without a lens, as well as others which are not. These larger grains may be of many different shapes and as many different origins, but most will be composed of Calcium carbonate. The commonest grains to be plainly visible are those which were usually formed by marine animals rather like some of our modern shellfish. After their death, the vast quantity of shells were either buried intact or carried around by currents and sometimes broken up and ground smooth. Some were eaten by fish, which had specially toughened teeth for grinding the shells, and then excreted as fine dust. Whatever their fate, the shells added substantial quantities of lime to the sediment and are often present amongst the other grains of lime (Fig. 36).

Oolitic Limestone

Another type of grain, which is very common in some beds of the limestone, is a small spherical pellet usually not more than 1 millimetre in diameter. These grains, which are called Ooids or Ooliths, meaning 'Egg Stones', are commonly found in some shallow-water tropical seas today. This gives us a clue about the origin of these particular beds of limestone and suggests that when they were formed they covered the bed of some shallow tropical sea. We know that, today, these pellets grow on the sea-bed assisted by the action of marine algae, which coat any tiny sand particles with layers of lime as a by-product of their own metabolism. After a while the weight of the sand grains may become sufficient to prevent them from being rolled around by the waves and currents, but more typically they are swept up by currents and buried by further deposits until extensive banks of tiny pellets accumulate. When cemented, the resulting limestone is called 'Oolitic'. Oolitic limestone can be found in many places in the Mendips and it is very well displayed in Burrington Coombe at the 'Rock of Ages' where it is known as the Burrington Oolite. You can see the Ooids in many of the loose pieces of rock around here but be sure to take a hand lens! (Fig. 37).

Burrington Coombe

A half-day spent walking the length of Burrington Coombe would be an excellent introduction to the Lower Carboniferous rocks. The oldest of these are the alternating beds of shale and limestone known (not unreasonably) as the 'Lower Limestone Shales', over which the Mendip streams flow before vanishing underground when they meet the main beds of limestone. One of these streams, the West Twin Stream, is found in the valley which joins the Coombe at its southern end close to Goatchurch Cavern and near the major bend in the road. The stream disappears underground near to this cave system and flows through underground passages which have been dissolved by the water. When you pass this point and enter the main part of the Coombe it becomes 'dry', i.e. all the surface waters have gone underground. The beds of limestone commence with the aptly named 'Black Rock Limestone'. This is very dark grey, even black in places, and is distinguished by numerous inclusions of silica in the form of chert nodules. These look rather lighter-coloured when weathered and often have a bluish sheen too. They are much harder than the limestone and very resistant to solution, so that they often stand proud of the rock surface by a few millimetres. There are many fossils in this horizon, including a quite common colonial coral called *Syringopora* and various brachiopods. Unfortunately the specimens to be found loose are becoming scarcer over the years, so please don't collect from here but be content to observe.

Calcite and Dolomite

Towards the top of this unit the rocks are sometimes rather discoloured, with brownish patches several metres across. These are places where the normal mineral, Calcite, has been replaced by another carbonate called Dolomite. This is a mixed Magnesium/Calcium carbonate and is often a secondary alteration product caused by post-depositional changes in the rock. The rocks at this level are called the 'Black Rock Dolomite'. This dolomitisation process sometimes gives an almost purely dolomitic rock which is often honey coloured. In general, this recrystallisation results in the original fossils being dissolved and destroyed, so that the rock appears to be devoid of any evidence for life. Originally, the fossils were probably just as numerous as in other beds but were replaced by crystalline Dolomite and lost without trace. Another effect that accompanies this recrystallisation is that of volume loss. Dolomite is denser than Calcite and the equivalent number of molecules of Dolomite which replace the same number of Calcite will be less voluminous. Consequently, there will be voids in a secondary Dolomite limestone and these give the rock a porous appearance as well as making it look distinctly crystalline, if the Dolomite grains are large enough.

Sea-shells and tropical lagoons.

There are some quite fossiliferous beds of limestone above the Black Rock Limestone and a search of the screes on the east of the road might well show some loose shell fragments of brachiopods and pieces of coral. These come from a small quarry opposite the beginning of a track which leads to Goatchurch Cavern. Towards the upper end of this series of rocks, i.e. lower down the Coombe, beyond the cave called Aveline's Hole (Fig. 38), there is a yellow/buff coloured band of Dolomitic limestone which traverses the eastern face of the Coombe, and which marks the beginning of the next major unit of rock. This is the Burrington Oolite which is well exposed at the 'Rock of Ages' (Fig. 39). Here you can see the ooids (or ooliths if you prefer), especially on weathered surfaces but also on clean broken ones, provided that you look very closely as they are rarely much more than one millimetre in diameter. These pellets of lime tell us that the rock was deposited as a loose assemblage of sandy grains, in a very shallow and rather turbulent sea, probably when the water depth was just a few metres. This is known by comparison with modern analogues in places such as the Bahamas Banks, and ooliths are commonly formed today in shallow tropical seas.

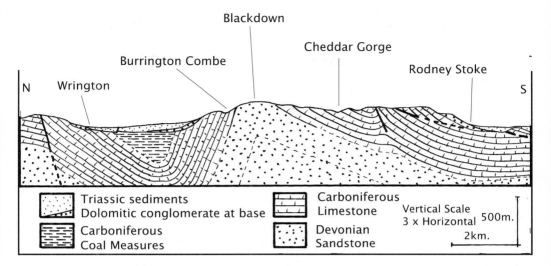

Blackdown

Cheddar Gorge

Burrington Combe

Rodney Stoke

N   Wrington   S

| | Triassic sediments | | Carboniferous
Dolomitic conglomerate at base   Limestone   Vertical Scale
                                                   3 x Horizontal 500m.
| | Carboniferous | | Devonian   2km.
Coal Measures   Sandstone

Above, Fig. 26: This section shows the combination of folding and faulting which resulted in the uplift of the *Mendip* Hills at the close of the Carboniferous Period. It is derived from the British Geological Survey 1:50,000 Special Sheet of the Bristol District.

Left, Fig 27: The deep quarry at Moons Hill, near Stoke St. Michael, is cut into Silurian ashes and lavas of andesitic compo-sition. Thanks are due to the quarry manager and owners for permission to visit.

Above, Fig 28: The fragments of explosively erupted rock in Moons Hill Quarry are evidence of the violent times which commence the geological history of Somerset.

Below, Fig. 29: The Mendip Hills must once have been far higher and before any erosion took place they may have reached around three times their present height.

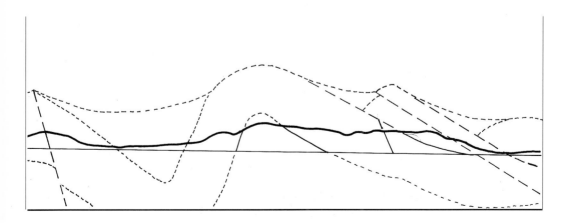

Above, Fig. 30: The junction between lower Carboniferous limestone and the overlying Jurassic Inferior Oolite is marked by a sharp erosion surface, or unconformity at the De La Beche locality in Vallis Vale.

Below, Fig. 31: The junction between lower Carboniferous limestone and the overlying Jurassic Inferior Oolite is marked by a sharp erosion surface, or unconformity.

De-La-Beche locality in Vallis Vale, Frome (ST756492):
View from south-west. Face ca. 8 metres high.

Above, Fig. 32: Two common shrubs which indicate a limy soil are the Wayfaring Tree, *Viburnum lantana* (left) and Spindle, *Euonymus europaeus* (right).

Below, Fig. 33: The highest ground in the centre of the Mendip anticlines, as here above Shipham, is formed of Devonian sandstones in which there is little or no lime. The resulting soil is highly acidic and poor in nutrients, supporting only grass and scrubby heather and bilberry and gorse.

Above, Fig. 34: Cheddar Gorge, seen from the south, is one of many similar ravines cut into the slopes of the Mendip Hills over 200 million years ago when the hills were being eroded in a desert climate.

Below, Fig. 35: The limestones of the Mendip Hills vary from coarse shell debris, through sand-sized ooliths to this fine-grained calcite mudstone from Burrington Coombe which shows conchoidal fracture.

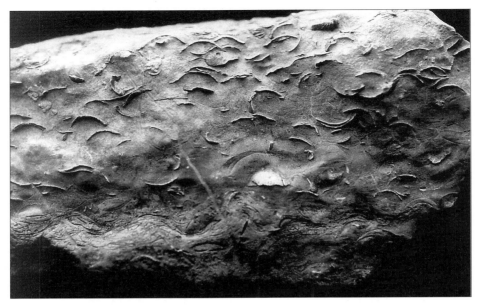

Above, Fig. 36: Shelly limestone, Lower Limestone shales, Burrington Coombe.

Left, Fig. 37: The Burrington Oolite is a particularly fine-grained example of the pellets that were formed by algae which coated tiny particles of silt and sand on the sea-bed. The matrix between the pellets is clear crystalline calcite, and formed after the pellets were buried and as the rock hardened by the addition of lime cement.

Above, Fig. 38: Aveline's Hole. This cave is clearly visible from the road through Burrington Coombe, and the entrance shows deep erosional holes in the roof formed by water under pressure.

Left, Fig. 39: The 'Rock of Ages' acquired its name after the famous hymn which was written by the Revd. Augustus Toplady whilst sheltering from a storm in the cleft of this crag. It is not known if he noticed that the rock is oolitic limestone!

Coral seas in Somerset

The sequence of sediments this far, starting with shales and moving on to dark muddy limestones, and now through shallow-water oolites, suggests an overall shallowing from a deep water start in the lowest beds. This is borne out by the appearance of coral colonies in the next horizon, the Clifton Down Limestone. The Clifton Down Limestone is rather poorly exposed at road level, but it can be reached high up on a steep bank on the eastern side of Burrington Coombe, if you are prepared to scramble up the grassy slopes (10-20 metres above the road, just a few yards north-east from the public toilets). It includes at least one coral-rich bed and if you are sharp-eyed you will see large masses of colonial corals of the genus *Lithostrotion*, up to a metre across (Fig. 40). Fortunately, these are on surfaces that no collector has yet been able to destroy and are partly hidden by small thorn bushes; long may they last! The presence of colonial corals of this type is strongly suggestive of shallow waters, since modern corals are in general dependent for their success on a symbiotic relationship with algae which live within their tissues. These *Zooxanthellae*, as they are called, are essential to the coral's vigour and most, although not all, modern corals contain them. They would, of course, require light to enable them to photosynthesize and this indicates that the corals were living within a few tens of metres of the sea's surface. Consequently the water had to be both clear and shallow during these times.

Hotwells Limestone

If the corals were not enough to indicate shallow waters, then the highest beds to be seen in Burrington, the Hotwells Limestone, should. These are very fine-grained muddy limestones, known as 'Chinastone' on account of their resemblance to porcelain. This type of rock does in fact have a 'ring' to it if you chink two pieces together, and is as smooth a textured rock as you will find, with a characteristic conchoidal fracture. This is the curving and smooth-surfaced type of break that you get in glass and other very fine textured materials, known as conchoidal because it looks a bit like the outside of a shell with concentric undulations.

The lithology of these rocks is not in itself proof of their origin from shallow waters but at the lower end of the Coombe, an old quarry at the end of the track behind the café displays limestones which were occasionally dried out during the time of deposition and which mark the end of the Lower Carboniferous era. These limestones have upper surfaces which were being eroded very soon after deposition, during the Carboniferous period itself. This is known because there are several of these surfaces and some limestone was still being deposited after the earlier erosion episodes. Such erosion surfaces are found in 'Karst' topography, which is named after a region of eastern Europe (western Slovenia) where this is well developed. This regional name has been applied in geological descriptions too. The characteristic features seen in this quarry are irregular upper bedding surfaces with boulders and deeply eroded hollows on a surface which here is often stained red by iron oxides. These were the last beds to be deposited in the limestone sequence and as we have seen, they mark the stage at which the sea was effectively reduced to depths within the tidal range and ultimately became subject to erosion, perhaps by rain water dissolving the surface. Similar irregular and rough surfaces are found wherever limestone is subjected to solution by rain water, and possibly also to sea washing over shallow reefs, and could be encountered on modern tropical coral islands, should you wish to seek out a modern example! (Fig. 41).

This section completes the sequence of Carboniferous limestone exposures but before you finish in the Coombe you should return to a small rock exposure just behind the public toilets. Here you can see boulders of limestone set in a red matrix of Triassic age (Fig. 42). These were deposited here after the Mendip Hills had been uplifted and eroded and demonstrate that the Coombe was a valley long before modern times, in fact during the Triassic period, ie. around 250 million years ago. Thus, when you walk up the Coombe you are walking up an ancient desert valley or 'Wadi'. Since this was in existence at the time when early dinosaurs roamed the earth, you might imagine yourself walking between these barren rocky cliffs in the baking sun, with the sound of heavy breathing audible around the next corner!

Marine life in Lower Carboniferous times: Corals

Returning to the subject of limestone, you will probably have noted that the larger grains of lime usually prove to be fossils of one type or another. In all probability the sea from which these limestones were deposited was as rich in life as many modern tropical seas, and the variety of known fossils is immense, with many hundreds of species recognised in Britain alone. Some of the commonest and most easily seen include corals, which are often colonial, and look rather like some small shrubby plant with many individual polyps making up the branches. These can be found almost anywhere and species are usually distinctive. Since individual species are characteristic of particular levels they can often be used to determine which particular horizon of limestone you are looking at. One of the earliest corals is a very simple solitary polyp which made a conical skeleton only 2-3 centimetres long. This genus, which is called *Zaphrentis*, is found in the lowest beds of the limestone (Fig. 43). You might find it towards the top of the Coombe but there are plenty of them exposed at Middle Hope, north of Weston-super-Mare. Later solitary corals are mostly larger and often resemble a cow's horn in both size and shape, due to their habit of falling over at regular intervals! This happened when the ever expanding and elongating coral 'skeleton' began to lean to one side and in correcting this lean it grew into a curve. This was such a regular occurrence that it has given the group the common name of 'Horn Corals'. A typical example is the genus *Caninia*, which also occurs at Middle Hope. Colonial corals lived alongside the solitary ones and early types such as *Michelinia* look like a chunk of honeycomb whilst others, e.g. *Syringopora*, look more like a tangle of strands of spaghetti (Fig. 44).

Brachiopods

Amongst the many other fossils that can commonly be found are the shells of a group of marine animals known as the Brachiopods, which although still extant, is now far rarer and has many fewer families, genera and species than in the Carboniferous. These shellfish were numerous and varied in shape and are usually seen as convex fragments, or occasionally as complete shells, often with distinct fine radial lines or ridges ornamenting the shell. They lived on the seabed, filtering the sea water to strain out the food particles and extracting Oxygen at the same time. They took many forms and some are useful in determining the age of a particular limestone bed, in the same way as the corals are. Commonest are the Productids, Spiriferids, Terebratulids and Rhynchonellids.

Crinoids

Another commonplace fossil, known as a Crinoid, can be so dominant in some beds as to give its name to the limestone. The animal, which looked a little like a starfish, was attached to the sea-bed by means of a long cylindrical stalk of Calcite. After death, the stalk collapsed into sections which are usually a few centimetres long and around one centimetre in diameter (Fig. 45). Larger examples up to several centimetres in diameter and possibly a metre or more in length can occasionally be found. The living animal was apparently a 'sociable' one, with many individuals crowding together and giving the impression of a stand of plants. The common name for these animals is rather misleadingly 'Sea Lilies', and refers to their long 'stalks' and flower-like 'heads'. Crinoidal limestone is widespread and a particularly pleasant, though rather remote place to see it, is on the tip of Brean Down (Fig. 46). A much more accessible spot is around the old mine workings at Charterhouse, just a short drive from the top of Burrington Coombe.

Algae

Another type of limestone of organic origin is usually entirely devoid of animal fossils and appears to be very fine mud with distinctive thin laminations. This limestone was laid down by algae which were living as a thin film on the muddy sea-bed. They seem to have flourished at times when the water was so shallow and warm that animals could not survive in it, either due to the high salt content or the lack of oxygen. The action of the algae on the already mineral-rich water was to cause the precipitation of lime which combined with the gelatinous layer of algae to produce these finely layered muddy limestones. Occasionally the algae flourished locally and produced mounds or columns, rather as small tussocks develop in grassy areas today as successful plants gain the advantage over their neighbours. These mounds can still be recognised in some algal limestones and are called Stromatolites. Algal structures similar to these in the Lower Carboniferous rocks are also found in rocks in Greenland which date back over 3000 million years, and this makes them the oldest known fossils. Algal limestone is rarely very conspicuous and is often a component in other types of limestone, but it can usually be recognised by its distinctive laminated appearance (Fig. 47).

Volcanic rocks of the Carboniferous

Interbedded with the Carboniferous limestone there are other rock types which were deposited during this period. Most notable of these are volcanic rocks which are found in the area around Weston-super-Mare. There are lavas exposed on the rocky foreshore at the southern end of the toll road from Weston to Kewstoke. These red and brown weathered rocks contrast with the pale grey limestones and were erupted as black basalts from local volcanic vents. Lavas which erupt under water give rise to rounded 'blobs' of rock rather than continuous flows and the resulting pile of lava 'blobs' is known as Pillow Lava (Fig. 48). Pillow lavas can be seen quite clearly on the shore close to Sand Point, at the locality known as Swallow Cliff. This is reached from the National Trust car park at the end of the road past Kewstoke, by walking over the headland and about 500 metres to the west. On the shore is a small bay in which are exposed not only the pillow lavas from an underwater volcano, but also ashes which were blasted into the sky before settling in the sea to accumulate as thick volcanic sediments (Fig. 49). These ashes have a very distinctive khaki colour, in marked contrast to the grey limestones above and below them, and being rather softer than limestone, have weathered away very rapidly, leaving deep bays where they are exposed. There are four localities where the volcanic rocks occur on the promontory of Middle Hope. Each of these exposes the same volcanic horizon separated by faulting, and they all display the same bed of

63

volcanic rock. Three are easily visited, although low tide is helpful, but the eastern, and the least exciting one, is inside MOD property and permission would have to be sought in advance. What is especially interesting is that the ashes get thinner towards this eastern end of the headland and since the only lavas preserved are at the western end, it is clear that the source of these rocks was towards the west (Fig. 50).

In one bed there are distinctive vertical 'burrows' made by shellfish called *Lingula*. These were buried rapidly by the ash and give an idea of the rate of ash accumulation since their burrows just kept pace with the sediment surface as the animals grew larger (Fig. 51). Associated with the volcanic rocks are limestones with many fossils and the section at Middle Hope is a good one to spend a couple of hours browsing over. Amongst those which you might expect to find are solitary and colonial corals (*Zaphrentis, Caninia, Michelinia* and *Syringopora*), various brachiopods (Spiriferids, Rhynchonellids and Productids), crinoids, bivalves and trace-fossils. Please remember that hammering rocks and removing rocks and fossils from here without specific permission is forbidden, as the site is an SSSI. Why not try taking a close-up lens with your camera instead?

What was the Mendip area like during Lower Carboniferous times?

The first sediments to be laid down in the area, after the deposition of the Devonian sandstones, were thick lime-rich muds which hardened to produce black shales with thin dark muddy limestones. These were probably deposited in relatively deep waters after submergence of the region beneath the sea. The mud blanketed the earlier Devonian rocks and gradually filled up the deeper parts of the sea until the supply of mud began to diminish, either due to the wearing away of its source, or a physical barrier preventing its transport into the region. This shows that there must have been a land mass not too far away from here during the earlier part of the Carboniferous period but that it was only supplying finer-grained muddy sediments to the sea. Even though the waters were apparently quite deep, the sea-bed probably continued subsiding, thus allowing great thicknesses of sediment to accumulate without filling it up.

In the clearer waters that resulted from the mud's gradual disappearance, the dissolved lime, which the waters contained in abundance, was deposited in greater quantities and the dominant sediment then became muddy limestone. The Black Rock Limestone, was the first major limestone to be deposited. At first these sediments were dark in colour due to their relatively high mud content but in time the supply of mud was reduced and the limestones were deposited in purer form from increasingly clear waters. The appearance of the region during the middle part of this process of sedimentation would have been rather similar to that of a modern tropical coral reef, with extensive lagoonal areas of fairly shallow water, and here and there, much shallower regions with almost emergent sand banks of dazzling white coralline sand. Towards the end of the period the white sediments would have actually risen from the waters, at least in places and at times, and there would then have been extensive, very barren and desiccated rocky platforms, which were dissolved and pot holed by the occasional rains. Images of modern coral islands at just above beach level are probably appropriate analogues.

The considerable cumulative thickness of the earlier shales and limestones would probably have quite quickly filled the sea water basin, even allowing for extra tectonic subsidence, had it not been for a compensatory mechanism which allowed the sea-bed to sink under the increasing load. This is known as Isostasy and is equivalent to the effect of adding a load to a floating object, such as a boat; the heavier the load, the deeper it rides in the water. When sediments are added to the earth's crust, the deeper rocks behave as a plastic substance and are sufficiently mobile to allow the rigid crust to sink deeper. For whatever reason, the sea continued to accept considerable thicknesses of limestone, so that the final total depth of sediments deposited could easily have exceeded the total depth of the water at any particular time. Indeed, it must have done, because eventually sedimentation overtook subsidence and by the time of the Hotwells Limestone the sediments began to be exposed to the atmosphere.

During the long period of time in which the limestones were being deposited, the area now occupied by the Mendip Hills, and indeed most of Britain, was a shallow tropical sea with shoals and banks of sediment being washed backwards and forwards by the ceaseless tides and occasional storms, with reefs appearing here and there, over which rich faunas of animals lived. In between the reefs were extensive lagoonal areas, sometimes with patches of corals and crinoids and other shellfish. Other parts were too shallow or salty for animals to survive but ideal for algae to grow. The climate was apparently similar to that of today's tropics, and the best modern analogues for the rocks of the Lower Carboniferous are found in places such as the Bahamas Banks and around the Florida Keys, where warm shallow seas are depositing lime, often in extensive lagoonal areas of only a few metres depth.

The wide variety of types of limestone reflects the changing conditions that influenced the sediments from time to time. Calcite mudstones are the product of very quiet waters, probably shallow lagoons in which algae sometimes flourished. The presence of algae indicates that light was available and therefore that the water was probably not more than a few metres deep. Oolitic limestones were laid down in slightly more energetic conditions where algae grew on grains

Above, Fig. 40: The corals seen in the mid part of Burrington Coombe are the colonial form called *Lithostrotion* which evolved well into lower Carboniferous times, thus showing that the rock is of a particular age.

Left, Fig. 41: At the top of the succession in the lower Carboniferous limestones of Burrington Coombe is a series of thinly bedded rocks some of which show erosion due to solution in rainwater. These demon-strate that the sea-bed was emerging from the water at times, possibly for prolonged periods, and rain was able to dissolve the hardening sediment. The deeply eroded and pitted surface has boulders and pebbles of limestone scattered over it, and is stained pink by a concentration of iron which infiltrated the bed after burial. It is named Karst after the region in Yugoslavia where this phenomenon is widespread.

Left, Fig. 42: The steep sides of Burrington Coombe were once covered by screes and the valley bottom was choked by loose debris and large boulders of limestone from the slopes above. Some of these are still visible, as here (just behind the public toilets) and are firmly cemented by a matrix of red Triassic sands and silts which show that the Coombe was here even in Triassic times, over 200 million years ago.

Below, Fig. 43: Amongst the many fossil groups found in lower Carboniferous sediments corals are one of the commonest. Solitary ones such as *Zaphrentis* (ca. 1cm. in diameter), shown on the right, are accompanied by colonial forms such as *Michelinia,* (each polyp ca. 1 cm. in diameter), shown left. Both are from Middle Hope, near Weston super Mare.

Above, Fig. 44: Syringopora is a colonial coral found only in the lower part of the Carboniferous limestone, seen here at Middle Hope, Weston super Mare. The colony is about 30 cm. wide.

Below, Fig. 45: The short sections of crinoid stems are the main component of some limestones.

Above, Fig. 46: Brean Down is a promontory of Carboniferous limestone which project westwards into the Bristol Channel. At its tip there is limestone composed largely of crinoid fragments.

Below, Fig. 47: Amongst the many forms of limestone, one of the commonest is that made entirely from the secretions of marine algae. These form mats and hummocks over the sea-bed, occasionally rising into mounds called stromatolites.

Above, Fig. 48: The volcanics at Middle Hope include pillow lavas, which were erupted underwater and which cooled into rounded 'blobs' or pillows. Here the lava includes gas-bubbles which are now infilled by white Calcite and is covered by ash.

Below, Fig. 49: The volcanic ashes at Middle Hope are deeply weathered to a khaki colour. They are composed of fragments of ash with occasional pellets of lava known as lapilli, and often include fossils and pebbles of limestone.

Fig. 50: The volcanic rocks are separated by faults and occur at four localities, two of which can be seen here.

of sand on the sea-bed. These grains were constantly swept around and acquired an even coating of lime until eventually, when the algae died, they were swept into banks and buried. Coarse shelly debris resulted from partial destruction of shells by a number of means; fish may have eaten them, they may have been subject to regular wave action, rolled in strong currents or broken during storms. Their presence, albeit smashed to pieces, shows that the general environment was good for animal life with adequate food and oxygen. Corals, amongst the most particular of modern marine organisms, would only have proliferated during times when the water was clear, warm, well lit and with good oxygen supply, since they probably used symbiotic algae in their metabolism.

The volcanic rocks found in the region demonstrate that the often tranquil lagoonal waters concealed a dramatic build-up of pressures in the earth's crust, which occasionally broke free to produce violent explosions of volcanic ash and submarine lava flows. These scarcely affected the continuous deposition of lime from the saline waters but they must have given the local shellfish a fright! Many of these can still be found where they were dropped from the volcanic cloud and rather like the poor victims of Vesuvius at Pompeii, were buried in volcanic ash.

The environment in the Upper Carboniferous

The finish of the limestone deposition marks the end of the Lower Carboniferous period and the beginning of the Upper Carboniferous, which in Somerset is largely concealed by younger rocks but is just visible north of the Mendip Hills in a few small outcrops. At the time of this transition, the dominance of the marine environment was finally overcome by renewed deposition of sands and muds. These were mainly derived from a land mass to the north and west which covered central Wales and the English midlands. This is known to geologists as St. George's Land. These sediments easily filled the marine basin to sea level and there followed a prolonged period of fluctuating land / sea levels when the area was alternately a shallow freshwater swamp or slightly more marine estuary. In this steamy environment grew the gigantic tree-ferns and horsetails of the Upper Carboniferous tropical rainforest. These plants were so prolific, and the swampy waters so anoxic, that their partially decayed remains accumulated faster than they could be destroyed by bacteria, and thick beds of organic debris were laid down. After prolonged burial these were transformed, first into peat, and then to lignite, and finally to coal. Today we still have this legacy of fossilised plant remains with their locked-in sunshine, just waiting for us to dig them up to burn. We have been doing so for barely 1000 years and already we have largely used up the most accessible part of the reserves which it took tens of millions of years to form.

Rocks from this period are not well exposed on the Mendip Hills but are found just to the north of them in the Radstock coalfield. You can read about the Upper Carboniferous in the chapter on the Radstock area.

Post-Carboniferous events in the Mendip region

Following the Upper Carboniferous coal swamps, there were prolonged periods of dry climate known as the Permian and the Triassic. During these times the area was uplifted, folded and eroded to produce the prototype Mendip Hills. These were created by very dramatic events which were centred on the region now occupied by Brittany in northern France and the areas extending to the east. The main feature which had an influence on Somerset geology during this episode was the gradual northward movement in southern Europe of the rigid upper layers of the Earth known as the 'lithosphere'. This movement met resistance from the north, which caused the compression of the surface rocks in the north / south direction, and they were folded into a series of elongate ridges and troughs, evidence for which can be traced from the Mendips all the way to the west coast of Wales. The land south of this line falls within a region which was on the northern limits of a mountain building event, known as an orogeny. The main mountains were on the line of the ridge of land now seen in Brittany, and the Mendip Hills can be thought of as the foothills to these former mountains. The term 'Armorican' is often applied to this orogeny but you may also come across the synonymous terms 'Variscan' and 'Hercynian', all of which refer to the one event.

The earliest post-Carboniferous scene would thus have been one of young, freshly uplifted hills, of perhaps more than 1000 metres in height. The climate would have been arid and the scene might have been similar to that in hotter regions of the earth where young mountains are being actively uplifted today, for example, the Atlas Mountains of north Africa. Weathering quickly removed the cover of Upper Carboniferous sediments from the crests of the folds and once the underlying limestones were exposed the occasional rainfall was largely channelled through the limestone in underground rivers running through caves and open gorges, much as it does today. This produced a landscape that would have been closely comparable with the modern one. There would, however, have been far less soil and vegetation and the surface would have largely been barren rocky scree and bare 'Karst' limestone.

Pebble and scree deposits

The rainwater run-off, which resulted from the lack of soil and plants, caused sheet floods and violent erosion to carry pebbles and boulders of limestone down the slopes. These were deposited in heaps at the foot of some of the major gorges, which they partly clogged, whilst some were left perched on the flatter upper parts of the hills. The sedimentary formation which these pebble beds form is known as the Dolomitic Conglomerate because of its content of Dolomite (Calcium/Magnesium carbonate). You can still find these well-rounded pebbles in many places and three or four exposures could easily be visited in an hour or two. One already discussed is the exposure of boulders immediately behind the public conveniences in Burrington Coombe. These represent the in-filling of the 'wadi'. Another altogether more congenial venue is the car park of the Wellsway Inn (ST546560), on the road which leads down to Compton Martin from the 'Castle of Comfort' public house. Here you can see the pebble beds overlying the limestone near the top of the hills and there are also some clear examples of iron-rich mineral deposits. Another famous locality is at Draycott (ST480510). This village has given its name to a very distinctive bed called, rather grandly, the 'Draycott Marble'. 'Marble' is only correctly used for limestones which have been recrystallised during metamorphic processes such as occur in mountain building episodes. This has not happened to the Draycott 'Marble' which remains a straightforward sediment but since it is rather more attractive than plain limestone it has been used in appreciation of its ornamental qualities and the term 'marble' seems more fitting. The Draycott deposit is not a conglomerate but is called breccia because the pebbles are often angular rather than rounded. This indicates that they were deposited quite soon after being broken from the solid rock and before any significant amount of transport. They were formed as scree deposits on the flanks of the hills. The fourth locality where you can easily see the pebble beds is at Blagdon in an old quarry just above the village (ST499587). Here you can see well-rounded pebbles in sloping beds poised part way down the hill slopes where they came to rest.

Some Mendip specialities

Early Mammals and Bone Caves

One of the many features for which the Mendip Hills are today celebrated is their underground cave systems. These result from the solution of the limestone by rainwater, which takes up air-borne gasses and soil acids to become weakly acidic. This process has been going on ever since the hills were first exposed to the atmosphere and was initiated in the Permian and Triassic periods. At that time the surface of the land was probably very barren and the bare rock exposed to the elements. On this inhospitable landscape some animals did venture, however. These included tiny insectivorous mammals which were the very first 'rivals' to the dinosaurs. Unfortunately for them, but happily for us, some of these diminutive early mammals fell into the cracks which had been eroded in the limestone and so registered their claim to fame as the first known mammalian fauna in Britain. Most of the fossil material from this period has been found in deep, narrow fissures which were opened up by weathering. Tiny animals which were unfortunate enough to fall into these crevasse-like slots would often be trapped, and eventually fossilised in the sediments which filled them. Their pathetic remains, jaw-bones, teeth and the like, are now studied by the dedicated researchers who have the patience for sifting thousands of sand grains for a single tooth (Fig. 52).

Curiously, after 200 million years of evolution, mammals are still falling down the same holes! By now the animals have grown bigger, but apparently not much wiser, and their not-quite-so-pathetic bones present a considerable problem to the overcrowded museums. So much so that many of them were simply left where they were by the excavators when the once famous Banwell Bone Cave was being dug out. If you are ever fortunate enough to gain entry to this cave you will, I guarantee, be amazed at the piles of bones still stacked around the walls, just as they were left when illustrated in the contemporary 19th Century engravings (Fig. 53 & 54).

Banwell Bone Cave is privately owned and although visits may sometimes be arranged, there are several excellent show caves into which you can go without any appointment. You don't even need your wellies and you can experience the excitement and mystery of this gloomy underworld in complete comfort and safety. Better-known caves are those in Cheddar Gorge and at Wookey near Wells, although there are many other caverns into which caving enthusiasts venture. You might like to join such a group but do not under any circumstances attempt to go caving by yourself or without an experienced leader and proper equipment. The caves of Mendip have been the subject of many a worthy text in themselves and are therefore not treated in detail here, but before moving on we should consider the importance of the underground drainage that caused them.

Drainage patterns in the Mendip Hills

The normal fate of rain which falls over most of the county is that it seeps into the soil. The soil-water slowly moves by gravity towards small streams and from them into rivers and then to the sea. In the Mendip Hills much of the rain which happens to fall on the high sandstone moors soaks into the very porous ground but heavy rain may run off them on the ground surface. Both soil-water and run-off then work downhill until they reach the height of the surrounding almost impermeable Lower Carboniferous shales, where they form wet and boggy ground. This boggy ground is seen wherever these shales are exposed and there is an excellent example on the hill above Shipham in the Gruffy Ground Reserve (ST450567). From here you can see the well-drained sandstone hill on the skyline to the north, then below that the scrub-covered upper slopes of the shales giving way to wet rush-infested boggy ground just south of the road and finally the dry 'gruffy ground' of the limestone to the south. This is an excellent demonstration of the effects of geology on the drainage and vegetation and is easily accessible by car and then on foot.

'Potato Stones'

For reasons which are not entirely clear, but must be related to the juxtaposition of two quite different rock types, i.e. carbonates and silicates, over most of the Mendips there is a concentration of minerals at the boundary between the Carboniferous Limestone and the Triassic rocks. This mineralisation commenced with deposition of salts from the sea-water that lapped around the hills in late Triassic times. These salts were originally in solution in sea water which soaked into the surface sediments but due to the arid climate they were left behind when the water was evaporated from the sediment as roughly spherical 'nodules'. Similar nodular crystal growths are found in modern deserts and sometimes form attractive crystal masses known as 'Desert Roses'. The original nodules formed in the Triassic rocks were made of a mineral known as Anhydrite, a crystalline form of Calcium sulphate. Anhydrite is perhaps most familiar as the raw material for plaster. Since the crystalline nodules were first deposited, the original Anhydrite has been subjected to various alterations which, in many cases, have converted the nodule into a solid ball of Quartz. In a few examples this is very beautifully banded with red layers of iron oxide and in other even rarer cases, is in the form of Agate. In the centre of these recrystallised nodules there is often a cavity and in this you might be fortunate enough to find clear crystals of Quartz. The variety of minerals in these stones is quite large and they have become recognised as semi-precious. Their local name is 'Potato Stones' which hardly does them justice, but in the Bristol area single crystals of quartz with a similar origin have been more excitingly named 'Bristol Diamonds'. It is a pity that a more accurate but equally acceptable name has not been coined for the Somerset examples but 'Recrystallised Anhydrite Nodules' seems to lack something! If you would like to see some of these local 'gems' you could try walking the ploughed fields anywhere around the flanks of the Mendips, where you should look out for extra hard, rounded, cream-coloured and red-stained stones in the red soils. The villages of Winscombe and Blagdon and Dulcote are a good bet, but please respect private property. A far easier method of 'finding' some would be to visit local mineral shops, where many displays exhibit good examples which have been found in the area. In some shops you might find one cut and polished and ready to take home, so don't forget to take your cheque-book in your rucksack! (Fig. 55).

The resurrected bed of the Jurassic sea

After millions of years during which they were dry land, the hills were eventually submerged under a shallow sea in the period known as the Jurassic and sea water again covered the region. The history of the Mendip Hills was completed for many millions of years and they were lost to view under a cover of Jurassic sediments. These rocks are exposed in a number of quarries and form the top few metres in the eastern area of the hills, notably around Frome. The earliest part of the Jurassic sequence, the Lias, is locally either absent or very poorly represented over the Mendip Hills. This is because the hills were still above sea level during this time and sediments were either never laid down, or if they were, were quickly removed again by erosion. Consequently the earliest Jurassic sediments found on the Mendips are rather thin and often sandy, reflecting the high energy environment in which they were deposited. They contain marine fossils, thus confirming that the area was covered by the sea. At this stage in their history, the hills became a series of shallow rocky shoals. It seems that the seas surrounding them were much deeper and if you were to imagine Somerset flooded to the depth of the hills this might not be far from the situation that existed in the early to mid-Jurassic. The waters eventually deposited several metres of silts, sands and limestones but during this period there was never enough depth of water to ensure the stability of the bottom sediments which were often reworked and eroded. This resulted in a number of episodes of erosion of the top of the hills and these caused the Carboniferous Limestone to be planed-off almost perfectly horizontally. If you now observe the junction between the Carboniferous and Jurassic limestones you will almost invariably see a perfectly flat top to the grey Carboniferous limestones, over which the pale yellow Jurassic limestones rest. The underlying grey limestones are usually seen to be well bedded and the angle of dip of these beds is often very steeply inclined to the horizontal. The Jurassic rocks, by contrast, are relatively flat. The angular break between these two units of rock is a classic example of an 'Unconformity' and the best known locality was described in the 19th Century by an eminent geologist, Henry de la Beche, and is now known by his name. The place to see this is in the valley of the Nunney Brook, where it runs through Vallis Vale at Hapsford, near Frome. A short distance from this site is another not to be missed, at Tedbury Camp, near the village of Great Elm. This area was stripped of its Jurassic cover in preparation for quarrying and the unconformity was beautifully displayed before operations ceased. You can now walk on the Jurassic sea-bed, a rocky platform, and see where ancient animals bored their way into the rock to find safety from predators and a secure, if anti-social, home. You can also see the planed-off bedding of the Carboniferous limestone which is tilted at a very steep angle to the horizontal, and you should be able to find fossils from both periods (Fig. 56).

Boring fossils by the thousand!

The surface of the Lower Carboniferous limestone is usually riddled with cylindrical borings about 2-5 millimetres in diameter, and to a depth of around 10-20 centimetres. There are also numerous pear-shaped holes bored into the limestone which were made by bivalves called *Lithophaga*, similar to modern 'Date' shells. We know that these were the animals responsible because we can still find the shells trapped in the holes, whereas the origin of the cylindrical borings is less clear, since we do not find the remains of their makers. Covering the surface in patches is a layer of attached oyster shells showing that the rock remained free of sediment for prolonged periods. Both the oysters and the boring organisms colonised the surface for a considerable time during which it was often eroded even further by marine action. This caused the earlier borings and shells to be removed and we can often find evidence for repeated phases of activity where later borings cut oyster shells, or earlier borings are partly

Above, Fig. 51: The ashes mixed with lime sediment to produce striped sediments in which animal burrows, such as these made by *Lingula*, are easily seen. Some shells of *Lingula* are also preserved.

Below, Fig. 52: The deep fissures which were eroded into the Carboniferous limestone during the Triassic period were death-traps for small animals, including some of the earliest mammals. These teeth are from such animals and are approximately one millimetre long!

Left, Fig. 53: Banwell bone cave is celebrated for the numerous prehistoric animals which died after falling through a hole in the roof, leaving a legacy of skeletal remains. The cave later became a tourist attraction, hence the decorative whale jaws over the entrance stairway, and is now privately owned. Thanks are due to Mr. John and Mrs. Margaret Haynes and Mr. Ron and Mrs. Yvonne Sargent for permission to visit and photograph the cave.

Below, Fig 54: The bones in Banwell cave were so numerous that some were left on site, neatly stacked to one side.

79

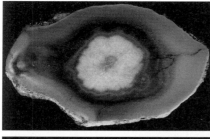

Left, Fig. 55: Potato stones are the silicified replacements of what were originally evaporite nodules of Anhydrite (Calcium sulphate). They are widespread around the Mendip Hills and found in the Dolomitic Conglomerate.

Below, Fig. 56: Tedbury Camp was a hill-fort in Vallis Vale. It was partly quarried (in the 1960's) and revealed an excellent example of the unconformity between the Inferior Oolite and the Carboniferous Limestone. Thanks are due to Hanson Aggregates for access.

Fig. 57: The erosion surface at Tedbury Camp is covered by millions of borings made by marine animals during Jurassic times. At this time the limestone was already well over 100 million years old and presumably as hard as it is today.

Fig. 58: This specimen from Mells shows the details of borings made by bivalves (pear-shaped) and worms (elongate). Thanks are due to the owners for permission to visit and collect samples.

Below, Fig. 59: At the De La Beche locality patches of oysters cover the borings showing that the sea finally returned to allow permanent colonisation.

Above, Fig. 60: The fossils found in the Jurassic rocks at Tedbury Camp include occasional ammonites such as this specimen of *Parkinsonia.*

Below, Fig. 61: The high ground of Ubley Warren above Charterhouse is cut by numerous 'rakes' or lead mines. These started as surface diggings along the lines of lead veins but soon went underground and became mines. Photograph courtesy of Mick Aston.

Fig. 62: The ore was smelted in nearby furnaces and the fumes passed through elaborate horizontal 'chimneys' or flues where the metals condensed from the cooling gases, to be collected later by scraping the walls. Arsenic was amongst the metals recovered this way!

truncated. All of this evidence demonstrates that this single surface represents an extended break in deposition, when erosion was the dominant force (Figs. 57, 58 & 59).

Lead, Silver and Zinc Mining

Rather like the Mendip caves, this subject has filled volumes, but whereas caves are not much more than holes in the ground where the geology has gone, mines are the sites of mineralisation, so I will devote more space to the Mendip mining industry. The metals that have been exploited commercially on the Mendips are mainly Lead, Silver, Zinc and Iron. The main economic minerals were Galena (Lead sulphide), Sphalerite (Zinc sulphide), and Haematite (Iron oxide) and Ochres (Iron hydroxides). Silver, being intimately mixed with the Lead, was only extracted after the ore was smelted. In addition to Silver, other metals could be recovered at this stage. Notable amongst these was Arsenic which, being volatile, was collected from the flues of the furnaces where it condensed.

The signs of mining are still very clear after many decades and even centuries have elapsed. The commonest sign is the hummocky ground which was left after the ore was dug and the waste dumped nearby. This 'Gruffy ground' is seen very well around the settlements at Priddy and Charterhouse, high on Blackdown and elsewhere (Fig. 61). The minerals which the miners sought were found in veins, i.e. infillings in the cracks in the limestone, which were caused by regional disturbances after the deposition of the rock. It seems from studying the sequence of events that the mineralisation is younger than the folding which created the hills and it even affects the Jurassic rocks which cover the hills, although usually only slightly. The majority, but not all, of the economic ores are restricted to within the Carboniferous Limestone itself, thus suggesting that the main period of emplacement was between the Carboniferous and the Jurassic periods, but it is clear that the process went on for a long time. The majority of mineral veins are found within the limestone. This is due to at least two factors, one being that limestone is heavily fissured by the solution of the rock and therefore has plenty of cavities suitable for mineral deposition. More important than this may be the fact that most minerals are more easily dissolved in acidic water than if it is alkaline. Since limestone is alkaline any mineral-bearing water which passes through it rapidly loses its acidity and with it the ability to hold the dissolved minerals, so they are deposited as the water becomes less acidic.

Mining techniques

The nature of early mining operations was simply a matter of digging a trench down from the surface wherever a vein of minerals was detected and then following the vein downwards and along its course. Due to their variable thickness in different places many veins became too thin to be followed far and the work might then cease. It required great faith and considerable capital investment to search even deeper for the same vein which had just vanished since no rewards would be immediately available, so mining was always a risky occupation. Mines became deeper with time and the ore treatment process developed to extract a greater proportion of the metal. The most conspicuous remains of this activity are seen at Charterhouse where there is an elaborate system of settling ponds from which the denser metal ores could be recovered after the rocks had been crushed and washed. These are found along the delightfully named valley of Velvet Bottom. In addition to the ponds, near Charterhouse you can also see the furnace flues which are a series of long tunnels, effectively a horizontal chimney (Fig. 62). The roasting of the ore caused some of the metals to be vapourised and later, as the vapours cooled, the metals were left on the walls and roof of the flues from where they could be scraped off by men or boys. One metal recovered this way was Arsenic. Imagine the working conditions and life-expectancy for a man or boy sent in to the hot, dry and dusty flues to scrape Arsenic off the walls!

Mendip Iron ores

Apart from the highly valued Lead which was used for plumbing, and Zinc which was used in its own right and for making brass alloys, and not forgetting the substantial amounts of Silver, the Mendip Hills also yielded moderate amounts of Iron. This was used for manufacturing edge-tools and agricultural implements, mostly around the Mells area, where the Fussells were a famous family of iron masters. There is an excellent account of this industry in 'Old Mendip' by Robin Atthill, published by David and Charles in 1964. Iron Ochres, a very colourful group of minerals, were used for pigments, and were dug from pits on the ground surface which remain to this day, as for example the Wurt Pit near Harptree. If you are rash enough to handle any specimens of this dull red earthy material, which is easy enough to pick up around the Harptree area, you will soon realise its potential as a pigment, and it will stay with you for the rest of the day! There are some good examples of iron ore still visible in the car-park at the Wellsway Inn above Compton Martin, where you will see steely-blue masses of Iron ore, together with red-stained soils and yellow Ochres. These iron ores may well have a quite different origin from the Lead and Zinc, since they appear to relate to the upper surface of the Carboniferous limestones, and are probably derived from the overlying Iron-rich Permian and Triassic rocks. This is apparent in the Wellsway Inn exposures, where the ochres are only seen in the pebble beds overlying the solid limestone, and are concentrated at the bottom of these beds, suggesting deposition from waters flowing through the pebbles, and over the solid rock.

Places to visit with special geological interest

If you wish to see a full range of the rocks of the Mendip Hills, you will need to make a number of separate excursions, ideally by car, and you should allow at least half a day for each one. There are perhaps four principal areas to aim for which are particularly interesting and accessible. These are: the coastline from Brean Down to Sand Point (which needs low tide and two or three visits to itself), the Blackdown area from Burrington Coombe to Cheddar Gorge (another two days worth), the Vallis Vale sections near Frome (at least a very pleasant half day here) and the Charterhouse and Priddy mining areas (again at least a half day). At each of these localities you will need to walk a mile or so to appreciate the variety of rocks. You would also have to climb up to at least half the height of the hills at Burrington Coombe (to around 200 metres O.D.) if you are to reach the Devonian sandstones, but there is a great deal to see almost at road level, so don't be put off. All of these areas are described in some detail in a regional excursion guide-book published by the University of Bristol and edited by R.J.G.Savage (1977), and you are recommended to make use of it if you can find a copy, although it is long out of print.

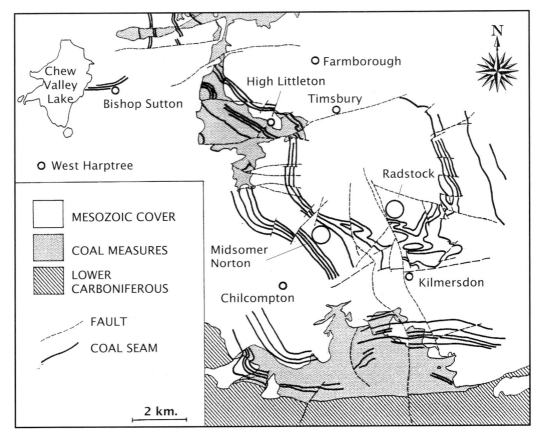

Fig. 63: The coalfields around north Somerset are scattered because they are isolated by folding and faulting and are also covered in many places by younger Mesozoic rocks. Thus, the Radstock coalfield extends more or less unbroken into the Chew Valley and is repeated in the Nailsea coalfield further to the west. There is a belt of highly disturbed strata near Farmborough which made mining extremely difficult, the seams often dipping vertically.

(This diagram is derived from the British Geological Survey 1:63,360 Sheets 280 and 281).

The Radstock Coalfield and Chew Valley

Geographical position

At first sight, these two regions seem quite different, indeed they are scenically so, but there is an underlying connection in the hidden rocks of the Coal Measures, which are upper Carboniferous strata. These extend throughout the area around Radstock and at least as far as Chew Magna. They do not reach the present coast however, as is proved by their absence from the base of the Triassic marls in a deep borehole sunk at the Weston-super-Mare Gas works. This hit lower Carboniferous limestones directly under the Triassic red marls, where the Coal Measures should have been. They must once have been present but were entirely eroded away before the sediments of the Triassic period were deposited. This shows that the once continuous coalfields of the north Somerset area were separated by the structural movements at the end of the Carboniferous period and by erosion which followed during Permian times. In the west they remain concealed by later sediments but in the east they are now exposed at the surface, hence the different scenic aspects. The west is low lying and soft contoured with gentle dip-slopes and rounded escarpments, whereas the east is higher topographically and has a relatively flat plateau-like appearance in parts. Some of this flat high-level topography is the remnants of the Mendip Hills. Pre-Jurassic erosion cut them down to a moderately flat surface, but deeper valleys cut through this landscape too, following the softer rocks of the upper Carboniferous. The scenery around Radstock is therefore a combination of high plateau and deep valleys.

The Radstock area is notable for its association with coal mining, the last pit closing in the 1970's. The coalfield was a very small one, its surface outcrop extending from just north of the Mendip hills at Mells to Stratton-on-the-Fosse. Although the surface outcrops are restricted, the coal-bearing rocks were found over a wider area to the north and west, beneath the cover of younger Triassic and Jurassic rocks. The first definite references to coal working in Somerset are from the 16th Century, although there is some evidence that it might have been used by the Romans at Bath as fuel in perpetual fires burned to honour Minerva. These earliest workings were presumably restricted to the areas of outcrop of the coal seams, whereas later the sub-surface workings took advantage of the shallower concealed areas. These shallow mines, working at depths of around

130 feet or even less, were quite numerous and are known from as early as the late 18th Century at Stanton Drew and Bishop Sutton. The Chew Valley sites have been well documented in a booklet published in 1976 by W.J.Williams, entitled 'Coal Mining in Bishop Sutton North Somerset c.1799-1929'. The history of the entire Somerset Coalfield is described in the book 'The History of the Somerset Coalfield' by C.G.Down and A.J.Warrington, published by David and Charles. They list no less than 79 separate collieries, spread over the area from Pensford in the north, to Tunley and Radstock in the east, Coleford and Nettlebridge in the south, and Farrington Gurney and Bishop Sutton in the west. This book is well worth looking at for the insight which it gives to the hazardous lives led by the miners, and the extraordinary difficulties that this contorted coalfield presented.

During its deposition the Radstock coalfield was clearly connected to others at Nailsea and in Bristol, but it has been separated from them by structural deformation since then, and is now isolated by intervening rocks. This deformation resulted in the coal-bearing strata being folded into broad troughs and arches. They are weak rocks by comparison with the underlying limestones, and could not withstand the pressures so well. Consequently they buckled and deformed within themselves, so that complex minor folds, and most importantly, thrust faults, cut through the shales and coal seams and caused them to become highly fragmented (Fig. 64). The angle of dip of the coal seams in many of the mines was about 1 in 3, but some strata were vertical, or even inverted! Some of the coal was in seams only around 60 cms thick, and this also made the task of mining coal a very difficult one. Working the coal in these conditions was sometimes done by the same techniques more normally used in lead mines, ie. by 'stoping'. This involves cutting away the coal overhead, allowing it to fall to the 'ground' and removing it, then setting timbers across the floor and standing on them to cut away the roof again. By this means the miners worked upwards, leaving a yawning chasm below them, with nothing but old timbers supporting them as they worked.

You might be surprised to learn that even in the 17th Century, the annual output of coal from Somerset was around 100,000 tons, and moving this amount of coal to towns such as Glastonbury, Wells and Bath created a problem almost as great as mining the coal itself. To overcome this difficulty, in the late 18th Century the Somersetshire Coal Canal was built and the Dorset and Somerset Canal was also attempted, although it failed soon afterwards. Both of these schemes have left permanent marks on the landscape and you can still see the Somersetshire Coal Canal complete with water and boats where it meets the Kennet and Avon Canal at Dundas, close to Limpley Stoke just south of Bath. In the mid 19th Century the annual production from Somerset was around 750,000 tons, (equivalent to many modern mines at their peak), and Somerset had become a nationally significant player in the production of coal. The level of production increased into the early 20th Century, when 1,250,000 tons was a typical annual output, but with the rise of the industrialisation of the Midlands and north of England, and the extraordinary difficulties experienced in Somerset mines, the industry began to decline and effectively came to an end in the 1970's. This could be attributed to many causes. The increasing use of machinery elsewhere was not so effective in Somerset's difficult mines and demands for local coal could not nearly be met by Somerset alone, so that other suppliers moved in to the market. But these problems were not new and in truth, the real cause of the extinction is a complex of factors. Political moves to develop nuclear power and the increasing use of gas and oil to fire power stations, removed the electricity generators' dependency on coal (and its notoriously 'troublesome' miners), and robbed the local pits of their main customer, the Portishead Power Station. The last few years of production at Writhlington and Kilmersdon collieries averaged around 250,000 tons annually, which still rivalled the earlier centuries' total output. This figure demonstrates that there is still plenty of workable coal under north Somerset and one day, no doubt, it will be re-discovered. Whilst the present generation of retired or redundant coal-miners may lament the passing of an age, their successors will honour them some day in the future, when they dig through their old works (Fig. 65).

Geological Summary

The rocks of the Upper Carboniferous, the period in which Britain's coalfields were deposited, are made up very largely of sand and mud grains. These combined in varying proportions to give a range of sandstones and siltstones, or when mud alone was deposited, the resultant rock was either a mudstone or a shale. The difference between these latter two is that mudstones are usually more or less devoid of lamination and break into blocky lumps, whereas shales are well layered into very fine laminae, and split readily into thin sheets. Shales are often confused with slates which have a very different geological history, being created by squeezing mudstones or shales very hard and causing new minerals to form. These new minerals include flaky micas, which cause the rock to split easily into thin sheets, often at a steep angle to the original bedding, whereas shales are always laminated parallel to the bedding. Shales are therefore often seen with fossils preserved on the flat surfaces, whereas slates rarely show fossils on the smooth splitting surfaces. Slates are metamorphic rocks, whereas shales are sedimentary. The environment from which these rocks were deposited was that of a very large estuary or broad swampy coastal plain, with the land very little elevated above sea level. This resulted in extensive areas of shallow water covering muddy or sandy sediments. The waters could be fresh, brackish, or salt, depending upon the relative land / sea levels. It is easy to imagine similar conditions today in areas such as the Everglades of Florida, although the extent of the Upper Carboniferous coal swamps was on a far greater scale than even this famous example.

The deposition of sands and muds fluctuated throughout the period of the Upper Carboniferous, on both short and long time-scales. The general trend during the period was from coarse sands and grits at first, towards finer grained silts and muds later on, but within the period there were many examples of fluctuating water velocity, which caused sediments of various grain sizes to be deposited. In general, the faster the water-flow the larger the grains that it can carry, so sediments that were dropped as currents slowed down would become progressively finer grained the slower the current.

Fossils associated with the sediments are often confined to specific horizons and these sometimes show regular fluctuations which are associated with the degree of saltiness of the water. In the rare examples of full marine conditions, fossils are found which are similar to those seen in the marine limestone of the lower Carboniferous. For example, the coiled shells of Goniatites, a group of marine cephalopod molluscs which are probably ancestral to ammonites, are occasionally found in these beds. These are frequently sandwiched between layers of shale containing a small brachiopod shell called *Lingula*. *Lingula* is still alive today, a rare example of an animal which has survived almost unchanged for many millions of years. It is today a marine organism, found on shallow tidal mud flats, and in the fossil record it is taken to indicate marginal marine conditions, so it is no surprise to find *Lingula* both before and after evidence of a marine incursion. Following the *Lingula* shells, there are frequently bands containing mussel shells. These are very similar to modern freshwater species and their appearance suggests that these sediments were deposited in fresh, or perhaps brackish waters. In the appearance and disappearance of different fossil groups, we have evidence for the progressive increase, and then decrease, in the salinity of the water, as the sea first advanced and then retreated again (Fig. 66).

During the episodes when the sea-water retreated, the sediments were often muddy and appear to have been laid down in very quiet, almost stagnant waters, which were probably similar to those of the swampy pools found today in deltaic areas near to the coast. These muds are usually rather poor in fossils but may contain plant debris from the rich flora that grew on the exposed ground in the region, and also yield the fresh water, or 'non-marine' bivalves, which are similar to today's river mussels. These small shells are often the only sign of animal life, although occasional fish and very rare amphibians have been found.

Life in the Upper Carboniferous

By far the most conspicuous fossils in these Upper Carboniferous rocks are the remains of terrestrial plants. These may be the stems, leaves or roots, or even on occasion the fruits of plants, which ranged from small herbs to giant trees. Many types have been described, and the number of species is impressive. It should be noted though, that the roots, stems and leaves are often separated from each other in the rock, and that many a tree has been given three names as a result, one for the roots, another for the trunk, and a third for the leaves! However, even allowing for this, there is a very substantial flora known from the Upper Carboniferous and these were amongst the earliest land plants in Britain, and certainly the first which grew to large size.

Many of the plants that are commonly found preserved are the leaves of tree-ferns which grew to the size of modern trees, with trunks up to one metre in diameter and many metres in length. These bore branches from which finely divided pinnate fronds of leaflets were suspended high above the swampy ground. The individual fern-like fronds often fell off into the waters around the trees of course, and were preserved in the oxygen-poor muds which accumulated in them. The tough waxy cuticles of the leaves were particularly resistant to chemical decay and biological attack, and are still found almost as they were first manufactured by the plants around 300 million years ago! The softer leaf tissues were more readily decomposed, but even these are represented as films of carbon-rich decay products which show up jet-black against the dark grey shales. The detail of the preservation of these plants is so perfect that it is often possible to recognise individual cells within them, and in the best specimens even the finest structures of the cell walls are seen (Fig. 67).

The trunks of the trees were not made of the dense wood seen in modern types, but tended to be hollow and tubular, with a large central pith cavity similar to that seen in some modern plants, for example the Horsetails, and thus were not so rugged as most modern trees. They sometimes fell into the swampy waters which quickly rotted away any pith cells and allowed sediment to flood into the pith cavity. This resulted in cylindrical sediment casts, which are the normal form of preservation, with a thin carbonaceous film of organic remains over the surface representing the living tissues. It is usual to find fossil trees preserved either showing the leaf scars on the outer surface of the cortex (the narrow band of tissues on the outside of the trunk) or without any organic tissue remaining, when only internal details are seen on the pith cast. Depending upon the nature of the sediment which filled the trees, they may be preserved in a crushed state and have an elliptical cross section, or more rarely, they may still be cylindrical especially if preserved in their position of growth, i.e. vertical.

The roots of the trees were not as solid as those of modern ones either, but were soft and fleshy, with a central conducting strand which lay within a softer 'rhizome'. The main branching rhizomes had true roots set all around them, radiating out into the sediment rather like the bristles on a bottle brush. The roots of different species are difficult to distinguish from one another, and most trees appear to have had closely similar root structures. They are almost all known by one name, *Stigmaria ficoides*, but this name must cover a whole group of plants with different leaves and trunks.

The smaller plants were just as well preserved as the tree ferns in some cases, and there are various types of herbs known from the coalfields, including some very attractive rosette-forming leaves on flimsy stems very reminiscent of the Bedstraws, and known as *Sphenophyllum*. There are also elongated parallel leaves of a plant which looks remarkably like grass, called *Cyperites*, although true grasses are much later plants which had certainly not been 'invented' in the Carboniferous but appeared in the Tertiary era (Fig. 68).

Anyone who has visited a tropical forest will, I feel sure, confirm that one of the drawbacks to an otherwise stimulating experience is the heat, the other being the flies of course! Life in the Upper Carboniferous was probably no easier and in the same sediments that yield the beautifully preserved remains of plants, there is no reason at all why insects should not be found. With this disarmingly optimistic philosophy, dozens of amateur palaeontologists, and a good few professional ones, have spent hours, indeed days, in all weathers, on hands and knees, searching the Radstock coal tips for insects. Why Radstock? Why at all? Well, this happens to be the main coalfield from which finds of spectacular insects were reported in the 19th Century. These included cockroaches, grasshoppers and harvestmen (the latter are not Insects but Arachnids, of course) and the most impressive of all, a dragonfly with a wingspan of two feet. Well, almost two feet! A pretty big one anyway. These giant specimens have so fired the imaginations of some palaeontologists that there are now over 1000 more specimens of insects known from the Upper Carboniferous in Britain than there were previously, an increase of about 400% in less than a decade. Why? All this effort was initiated by one man, known as 'Ed', properly addressed as Dr Jarzembowski. He, with the help of others, organised the systematic search of the old coal tips as they were re-worked for waste coal during the times of the miners' strike in the mid 1980's. The finds illustrated here are very largely thanks to his determination, and of course, to the sharp eyes of many volunteers who helped to search the tips (Fig. 69).

The insects look surprisingly familiar, especially in comparison with some of the plants, which are in general rather different from most common modern forms. The insects come from relatively few groups however, and it seems that the main ones to be found in the Upper Carboniferous swamps were cockroaches.

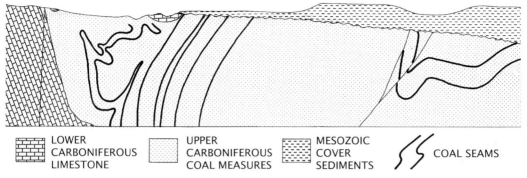

LOWER CARBONIFEROUS LIMESTONE	UPPER CARBONIFEROUS COAL MEASURES	MESOZOIC COVER SEDIMENTS	COAL SEAMS

2 km   Vertical scale x 3

Above, Fig. 64: The Coal-Measures of the Radstock Coalfield are crushed and contorted by the Hercynian earth movements which affected all of the Palaeozoic rocks of the county, and these soft ones most of all. Redrawn from BGS sheet 281, Frome, @ 1:63,360.

Below, Fig. 65: The head works of the collieries of the Radstock coalfield are all gone now but this old photograph shows how the New Pit at Bishop Sutton once looked. Apologies to the owner, but the author has no knowledge of the source

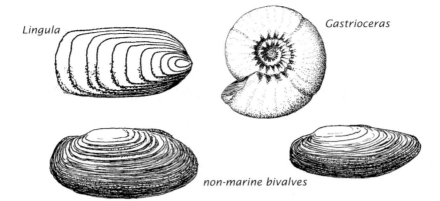

Lingula

Gastrioceras

non-marine bivalves

Above, Fig. 66: In the coal measures there were occasional marine influxes when subsidence allowed sea-water to flood the coal swamps. In the sediments which then settled, marine animals such as *Goniatites* (early ancestors of the ammonites) and the tiny brachiopod *Lingula*, which is still a living genus today, were preserved, sandwiched between beds with the non-marine bivalves such as *Carbonicola* and *Anthracosia*. The bivalves and *goniatites* are often identifiable to species level and are very useful for determining the precise age of the sediments and thus for predicting the appearance of coal seams.

Below: Fig 67: The plants which fell into the swamps were sometimes preserved in remarkable detail. All of those figured here come from the Writhlington colliery. The genera include: a) *Mariopteris (top left)*, b) *Alethopteris (top right)*, c) *Annularia (bottom left)*, d) *Lepidodendron (bottom right)*.

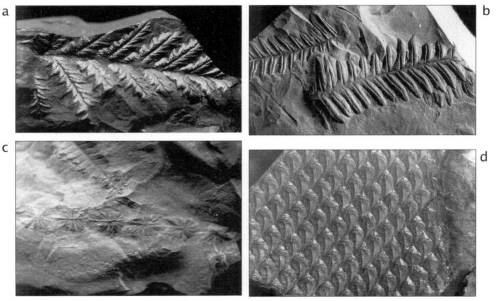

a

b

c

d

94

Left, Fig 68
Herbaceous plants from the Coal Measures at Writhlington colliery include *Sphenophyllum*

Below, Fig 69: The insects and other arthropods found in the Coal-Measures of the Radstock area have become justifiably famous in recent years, as they are often preserved in great detail. They include cockroaches, grasshoppers, dragonflies, harvestmen and spiders. They are rarely more than one or two centimetres long and look similar to fern pinnules but close examination reveals the veins in their wings or other ornament. The drawing a) shows a complete wing from a cockroach-like animal (top left), the photograph b) is of a wing from a grasshopper-like insect (bottom left) and c) is of a 'harvestman' type of spider-like animal (bottom right).

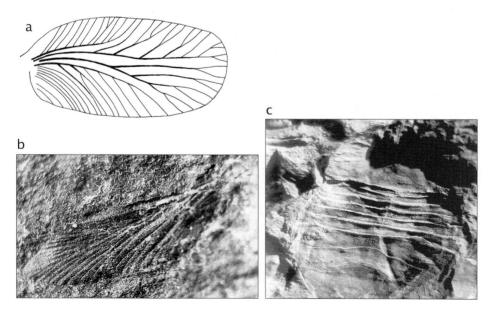

Right, Fig. 70: Although few body fossils of vertebrates are known, the presence of a footprint is undeniable proof that something once walked, or crawled, in the Radstock coal swamps! This footprint is around 6cms long, so an animal about 25-30 cms long is quite possible.

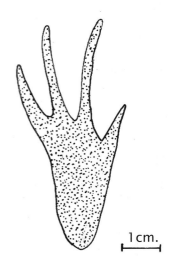

1 cm.

Right, Fig. 71: The coal seams occur in regularly repeated cycles of a predictable series of sediments. Following a coal (upwards) there is often an incursion of marine sediment, with goniatites or *Lingula* present. (Marine bands such as this are rather scarce in the Radstock coalfield, but examples are known). After the marine submergence the sediments are mainly fine muds, but these gradually become more and more silty, and finally sandy, as the submerged area filled up with sediment, and eventually plants colonised the shallow swampy water once more, leaving their roots in the seatearth and above that the next coal seam. The complete sequence is called a 'cyclothem'.

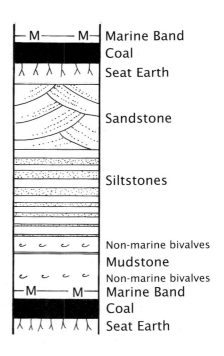

M——M Marine Band
Coal
Seat Earth

Sandstone

Siltstones

Non-marine bivalves
Mudstone
Non-marine bivalves
M——M Marine Band
Coal
Seat Earth

Above, Fig. 72: After the mines were closed the remaining tips gradually grassed over, and some were re-worked in the 1980's to extract the unsorted coal from them. The few remaining tips are curiously out of place today, and resemble small volcanoes. This one is close to Midsomer Norton.

Below, Fig. 73: The flat-lying Mesozoic rocks of the upper Chew Valley form table-like hilltops with gently dipping slopes and steep edges.

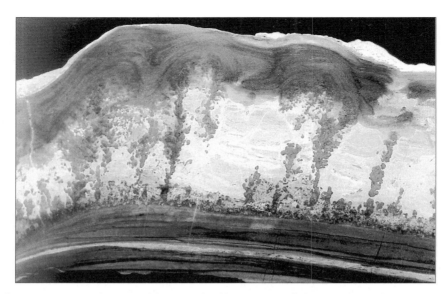

Above, Fig. 74: Cotham Marble is an algal limestone of Rhaetic times, (late Triassic), which shows the growth structures of the algae when cut vertically. The resemblance to trees and hedgerows is so strong that the rock is called 'Landscape Marble'.

Below, Fig. 75: The top surface of Cotham Marble develops lumps and ridges where the algae grew away from the mud surface, and these form characteristic 'nobbly' shapes which have been used ornamentally.

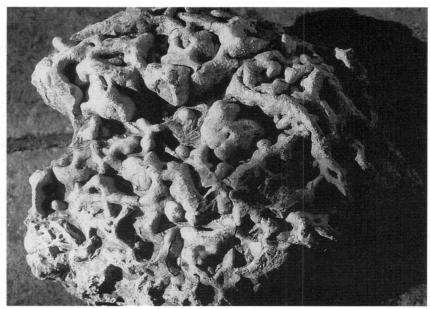

Left, Fig. 76: The type locality for Cotham Marble is Cotham Hill in Bristol, where this is one of a pair of obelisks decorated with the local stone. Sadly, it is largely weathered away now, few panels remaining intact, but most being replaced with carved blocks of plain stone.

Below, Fig. 77: A small example of an ammonite from Dundry Hill, the source of countless specimens in the past.

These can be imagined to have scuttled about in the leaf litter, eating the decaying remains that they were surrounded by. Grasshopper-like types also occurred, presumably enjoying the grass-like *Cyperites* clumps. There were also the inevitable predators to look out for, notably the giant dragonflies and the arachnids. The latter were fearsome beasts, one type of spider having a well-armoured abdomen which is very well preserved in the shale. The size of the dragonflies is legendary, rumoured to be about two feet in wingspan. In fact, I have seen the best known specimen, and from memory it is nearer 9 inches along one wing, but that still makes it a formidable insect the size of many a model aeroplane! This giant size perhaps reflects the absence of any more sophisticated flying competitors. There were no bats or birds, nor even pterodactyls at this time.

Although there are very few records from the area, there is at least one specimen of a vertebrate footprint from the Radstock coalfield, which suggests that amphibians lived in the swamps, and from analogy with other coalfields in Britain and elsewhere, it is reasonable to suppose that these were the highest form of life at the time. Although the Radstock specimen was quite modest, the foot was apparently only a couple of centimetres or so wide, they are known to have grown to considerable size in other coalfields, perhaps to two metres in length in extreme cases. These amphibians were probably the ancestors of the reptiles which developed the ability to leave the swamps and to live on dry land (Fig. 70).

The Upper Carboniferous Cyclothems

The least voluminous, but most important part of the Upper Carboniferous rocks is, of course, the coal. This is an unusual rock in that it contains no minerals at all, but is composed entirely of the decayed remains of plants which are solidified into a few substances called 'macerals'. These include material from the coarse cellular tissues which looks like charcoal and gives coal its 'sootyness'. Another, which represents the gelatinous decayed products of softer tissues, appears shiny and glass-like, and is clean to the touch. Other components include the waxy cuticles of leaves and the abundant spore cases, which were the early equivalent of pollen. All these components combine to give the usual bituminous coal, which is typical of this area. The coal seams are not very thick, often less than a metre from top to bottom, but this represents a considerable quantity of plant debris, and therefore of elapsed time, during which no terrestrial sediment was able to penetrate the swamp. This gives some indication of the unchanging scene that the swamps must have portrayed, with almost perpetual damp and gloom from the overhanging fronds, the choked-up forest floor covered by rotting plant stumps and logs. The air perfumed by smells of soggy decaying vegetation, and in the drier areas, scuttling cockroaches and other creepy things crawling through the vegetation!

The various sediments which enclose the coal seams are usually found to be laid down in a sequence which is repeated, with another coal seam sandwiched in each sequential unit. Sometimes the range of rock types is incomplete, but in other examples we might find all of the normal varieties of rock preserved between two coal seams. Typically, above a coal seam we may find mudstone or shales. These may contain few fossils, or may include a marine fauna in a narrow band, often only a few centimetres thick. This may then be followed by beds of muddy or silty rock full of non-marine mussels, and then shales which may contain few fossils other than plants. Any of these beds may be absent altogether. The usual full sequence finishes with a pale coloured mud, silt or sandstone horizon, with a coal seam immediately above it. This pale coloured band is a de-mineralised 'soil' which underlies most coal seams, and in which the roots of the coal forming plants can still be seen. This bed is known as the 'seatearth', and because it has few soluble minerals left in it due to the removal of these by the plants, it is highly refractory, ie. it has an unusually high melting point and is suited to making certain types of ceramics, notably fire-bricks. In some 'coal' mines in Britain the most valuable product was the 'fire-clay' under the coal, and kilns are frequently found close to the coal mines, which of course supplied the fuel! (Fig. 71).

What can you see at the surface in the Radstock coalfield?

Having tried to enthuse you with the prospect of studying the rocks of the Upper Carboniferous, it is regrettably necessary to point out that, since many of these are very soft, they have weathered away more readily than their neighbours, and in general now occupy areas of low ground. The result is that few of these rocks are normally visible at the surface and we rely for exposures on the occasional stream section or chance temporary diggings made by Man. Apart from the rather rare natural outcrops, the waste tips from the old mines are amongst the most obvious reminders of the period and some very conspicuous conical tips are still visible, as at Camerton, Midsomer Norton and Pensford (Fig. 72).

The rocks which are most likely to be exposed naturally are those which are hardest, and these are the sandstones. These dominate the lower part of the Upper Carboniferous system and they might be expected to be readily visible. In fact there are only a few places where you can see them in exposures but the drab grey/brown stone was often used for buildings in the area of outcrop. The softer shales are even less likely to be exposed naturally, due to the ease with which they are weathered and covered by surface debris, but they are still easily recognised in the old waste tips from the coal mines, which appear out of the landscape like miniature volcanoes. Unfortunately, these spoil tips are normally too weathered to yield sufficiently large lumps of rock to contain more than fragments of plant, and perhaps insect, fossils. However, if you are fortunate enough to come across these shales being re-worked, it is very likely that you will find plant remains, often remarkably well preserved. There is one deliberately preserved area of such shales at Writhlington, which has yielded vast numbers of fossils over the latter decades of the 20th Century.

If the exposures of the coal-bearing rocks of this area fail to impress you, then maybe the cover of Triassic ones will do better. These rocks are found in the upper parts of the Chew Valley, a broad fertile valley which lies immediately south of Dundry Hill, only a few miles from Bristol (Fig. 73). The higher ground at the eastern end of the valley, around the villages of Priston, Farmborough and Marksbury, is caused by the resistance to weathering of hard beds of limestone and also by the underlying structural deformation of the rock. These limestones are interbedded with grey marls and shales of the period known as the Rhaetic, which marks the end of the Triassic; a period of time noted in Britain for its red-stained sediments. The red rocks of the Triassic give rise to a distinctive feature of the local landscape, as they produce red soils over the eastern end of the upper Chew Valley. These red rocks are followed chronologically by the Rhaetic rocks, which are characterised firstly by a band of pale greenish-blue marls known in the literature as 'Tea-Green Marls', and followed by a mixture of pale cream coloured limestones and dark grey to black shales. Few of these rocks is hard enough to justify being used in building and since they are largely covered by soil, you will not see much of them. However, if you drive around the area you can often see in the older buildings a mixture of red Triassic sandstones, pale cream limestones and sometimes, the grey-buff sandstones from the Upper Carboniferous.

We shall see more of this red Triassic rock and its succeeding Rhaetic limestones and shales, in the section on the shore around Watchet, but in this inland area there is one rock in particular which deserves special mention. This is the famous Cotham Marble. Cotham, a district in central Bristol, is situated on a hill and the underlying rock is largely limestone. Although Cotham Marble is rarely more than 20 centimetres thick, it and a few other beds are together hard enough to make a strong feature in the scenery, and a number of fairly flat-topped, low hills owe their existence to these limestones, for example, the area around Burnett, south-west from Bath. The Cotham Marble was deposited by the action of microscopic algae, which grew in shallow sea-water at a time when the Triassic landscape was first being covered by the advancing sea. The texture of the rock is its most distinctive feature. It is extremely fine-grained, being made up entirely of mud-sized particles and it has very fine laminae preserved in it. When cut in vertical sections, these laminae can be seen to start off fairly flat and smooth at the bottom of the bed. However, as we follow them upwards, they become corrugated and soon they form tall pillars. These are not smooth-sided but rather lumpy, and they look strikingly similar to trees, especially (to those who can remember them), to the English Elm. They in turn are covered by further smooth laminae. The whole rock has suggested to generations of geologists the appearance of a landscape with fields, hedgerows, trees and a settled, if cloudy, sky. The popular name for this rock is, not surprisingly, 'Landscape Marble' (Fig. 74). It can be found all around Bristol, for example near Pucklechurch (north of the River Avon), around Keynsham, at Burnett, and also further west at Barrow Gurney. This widespread distribution suggests that a large shallow area of water was covered by algae during the time of this particular bed's deposition. This is confirmed by the occurrence of similar rocks many miles further north, on the banks of the River Severn near Aust, and at Sedbury on the western side of the river. Clearly, during the late Triassic there was very extensive shallow water all over the Bristol region. Such algal limestones are very rare today and only form in waters where other life forms are restricted by the difficult conditions. Generally, hypersalinity is the most obvious hazard to higher animal or plant life, but very high temperatures, as found in volcanic springs, also encourages such primitive life-forms. The inference is that the Cotham Marble was deposited during periods of hypersalinity when the sea first invaded the arid landscape (Fig. 75).

The Cotham Marble is a very attractive rock which has long been valued for use as a decorative facing to outdoor stone work and as an inlay in fine stone fireplaces, tables etc. You will be fortunate to find any in the field because it is often collected whenever exposed, but if you are ever in Bristol take a look at the obelisks which stand on Cotham Brow (Fig. 76). These are faced with blocks of the Cotham Marble and show its characteristic lumpy surfaces well. You will find sections of the stones, cut and polished, in many mineral shops and museums. Although its natural upper surface is often very irregular and lumpy, due to the unequal growth of the algae, by contrast the lower surface is always smooth, and is usually gently arched, perhaps due to the lateral pressure of the expanding algal mat forcing the soft sediment up into a dome. The significance of the rock for the interpretation of the ancient environment is great, since it clearly demonstrates the fact that the late Triassic was a time of marine advance over southern Britain.

Whilst you may not come across many specimens of highly-prized Cotham Marble lying around loose in the fields, there is more than enough of interest to make a visit to the Chew valley worthwhile. The flat floor of the valley emphasizes the elevated areas on its flanks and these demonstrate very clearly the effect of harder rocks on the landscape. The modest hills of the eastern end of the valley are dwarfed in the west by Dundry Hill, a mass of Jurassic rocks capped by limestone, which effectively divides the Chew valley from that of the River Avon, which flows through Bristol. Dundry lies just a few miles south of Bristol, which it overlooks. This is the northernmost site from which ammonites were commonly found in the Oolitic limestone of the mid-Jurassic in the 'good old days' of local quarrying. Although rocks of the same age are found much of the way from the Dorset coast to the Cotswolds, the last ammonites are seen in abundance at Dundry. It seems that there was some almost impenetrable barrier to the movement of ammonites further north than Dundry, and that they were limited to the southern area by the geographical conditions. At this time, the Bajocian of the mid-Jurassic, there was relatively deep water south of the Mendip Hills, whereas to the north the evidence is for very shallow water with quite frequent drying out of the sea-bed. It is hardly surprising that the ammonites, with their fragile shells, perhaps chose to avoid the wave-washed shallows of the Cotswolds (Fig. 77).

Dundry Hill is not endowed with many quarries, and most are now overgrown, so the formerly abundant fossils are not easily found. However, there are sites where the top of the hill has been dug through for various reasons, some modern, such as road widening, and others much more ancient, for defensive purposes. In these it is still possible to find loose rocks and because the fossils are so very abundant, even these loose pieces will often show many species, although you will be lucky to find whole specimens. On a short walk to one such site I found the following: Bivalves; including oysters (possibly *Isognomon*), a large scallop *Ctenostreon*, a small scallop *Entolium*, another bivalve called *Trigonia costata*; Brachiopods, including *Acanthothyris spinosa*, and *Sphaeroidothyris sphaeroidalis*; a sea-urchin, *Clypeus ploti*; belemnites (probably *Acrocoelites*), the gastropod *Bourguetia saemanni*, and a fragment of an ammonite! The oysters were still cemented to the flat surface of the limestone, where they had lived. This is a very important indicator of the environment of deposition of this rock, because it proves that during its deposition, the oolitic limestone sequence was interrupted. At these times, erosion removed some of the earlier sediment and oysters were able to settle on to the hard surface (evidently it was already cemented together as rock) and to live to maturity without being buried by more sediment. This shows us that the area was unstable and that deposition of sediment alternated with erosion. No doubt the waters were very shallow and this, of course, could explain why ammonites found it difficult to swim further north. For more detail of this period look at the section on Vallis Vale, in the chapter on the Mendip Hills.

If you should find yourself walking high on Dundry Hill on a clear day, be sure to take a good look at the surrounding scene. I doubt if you will be able to avoid it anyway, since the views are really remarkable. The Chew valley is clearly laid out below your feet and the lakes help to pinpoint some of the very well-concealed settlements. From here you can see all the way along the Mendip Hills, from the Radstock area to Weston-super-Mare, and through the occasional lower gaps you can see down into central Somerset. If it is really clear you can also see across to the west of the county around Minehead, and over to south Wales, down well past the cliffs of lower Jurassic rocks at Penarth, and inland to the Black Mountains. Further north is the Forest of Dean, May Hill, and maybe even the Malverns if conditions are perfect. It makes a wonderful vantage point, and is blessedly free from cars or disturbance.

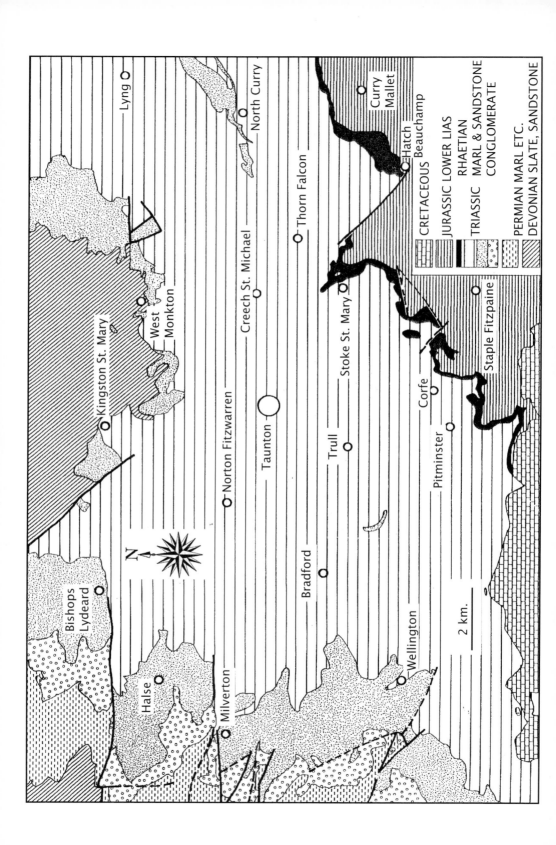

CRETACEOUS

JURASSIC LOWER LIAS

RHAETIAN

TRIASSIC MARL & SANDSTONE

CONGLOMERATE

PERMIAN MARL ETC.

DEVONIAN SLATE, SANDSTONE

N

2 km.

Lyng

North Curry

Curry Mallet

Hatch Beauchamp

Thorn Falcon

Creech St. Michael

West Monkton

Kingston St. Mary

Stoke St. Mary

Staple Fitzpaine

Norton Fitzwarren

Taunton

Trull

Corfe

Pitminster

Bradford

Wellington

Bishops Lydeard

Halse

Milverton

The Vale of Taunton Deane

The wide vale of Taunton Deane stretches from the foot of the Blackdown Hills to the Quantocks (Fig. 79). It is sheltered and fertile with rich grazing and arable land and, unsurprisingly, is also densely populated, with Taunton at its centre and Wellington a few miles to the south. Both are bustling towns and apparently ever-growing. The vale ends on the coast at Watchet.

Geological summary

The low elevation of the vale is the consequence of the softness of the rocks which underlie it. In the west these are the red marls of the Triassic period and in the east the lower Jurassic shales. Both of these rocks are little more than consolidated mud which readily softens on weathering to give a moist clay soil. In the past, the vale must have been very wet and possibly even under water some of the year, but with improved drainage it now supports a thriving agriculture. The softness of the rocks in the vale means that there are few exposures at the surface because the rocks are covered by their own weathered debris, so we can only find rocks exposed in rare stream sections, road-cuttings and pits. The exceptions to this general rule are those rocks which are hard enough to resist weathering and remain above the general level, and there are just a few examples of these. One of the most striking of the natural exposures is that of the basal Triassic conglomerates, which appear in the south-western corner of the region. These are pebble-beds, with quite thick units of very coarse pebbly sandstones, alternating with ordinary sandstone and silts. All of these are conspicuously stained red, due to the presence of the iron oxide, Haematite. The best place to see the pebble-beds is around the attractive village of Milverton. Fortunately, Milverton has a by-pass, and it is alongside this that you can see cuttings which expose the pebble beds, although you should be careful not to pull up on the road itself, but park nearby in the lay-by. (I would also ask you to be very careful not to endanger yourself or other road-users by standing too close to the carriageway, or causing an unnecessary distraction to motorists). (Fig. 80).

Opposite: Fig. 78: The vale of Taunton Deane is the low lying area between the Quantock Hills and the Blackdown Hills, bordered by the rising Brendon hills to the west and merging with the Somerset levels in the east. (This map is drawn from the British Geological Survey 1:50,000 Sheet 295 and 1:63,360 Sheet 311).

The pebbles in this conglomerate are very well rounded and made of hard rocks such as quartzite, so that they are very durable. They weather out separately and can be found in the soils locally, where they look just like any other pebble, despite having been shaped over 200 million years ago. These exposures are the inland equivalent of the more famous Budleigh Salterton pebble-beds, exposed on the coast some thirty or more kilometres to the south.

A short distance outside Milverton, close to Farthing's Farm, there are some old quarries which preserve in their faces the entrances to some narrow but persistent fissures, opened up in places into caves. If you are feeling adventurous, you might be tempted to explore the caves which are formed along these cracks in the pebble-beds. They are very narrow fissures but although they are very easily accessible, they need an experienced leader and considerable agility to penetrate to any depth. They are remarkable for their exploitation of natural fissures caused by jointing of the rock, which apparently must contain quite an amount of lime, allowing solution to open a significant crack. Although not spacious, it is said that the caves can be followed for several hundred feet in from the quarry face and that you can easily stand up in the inner chambers. This information was first given to me by Frank Hawtin, a very good friend of many years acquaintance, who persuaded me that we should try to reach the cave under his house, Quaking House. My limits were soon reached when I was firmly stuck between two walls about 30 centimetres apart, and only a few metres beyond the first tight spot, so I have not personally confirmed that the caves do extend under the house, which stands about 500 metres from the entrance, but the system certainly runs in its general direction. The plan of this cave system demonstrates very clearly how the passages are following a pattern of joints in two main directions. These caves are at an early stage of development, when the natural joints are just being opened, unlike the larger caverns seen in the Mendips, where the original fissures are often expanded beyond recognition (Fig. 81).

Returning to the fresh air after a trip underground, albeit brief and unadventurous, is an experience which I find renews the enthusiasm for even quite ordinary scenes, and I am sure that you will delight in the soft richness of the vale of Taunton Deane which, despite the scarcity of good rock exposures, still has many charms. There are other rocks to be seen of course. Just outside Milverton there are very good exposures of red sandstones of Triassic age, on the roadside a mile or so from the town on the way to Taunton, but the section is on a dangerous stretch of road, so don't try to stop there but get someone to drive you past. You will also see other small sections in the area as you travel around and these are enough to give a good idea of what the local rocks are like. In any event, you can always look in the ploughed fields where there are younger

Above, Fig. 79: This aerial view of Taunton Deane shows the flat topography.

Below, Fig. 80: The lowest beds of the Triassic era are coarse pebble conglomerates with well-rounded pebbles of quartzite predominating, seen here at Milverton.

Left, Fig. 81: The caves at Milverton are little more than fissures, opened along vertical joints in the sandstones.

Below, Fig. 82: The latest Triassic rocks show deep polygonal cracking where they dried out after having been submerged by the first incursion of the sea.

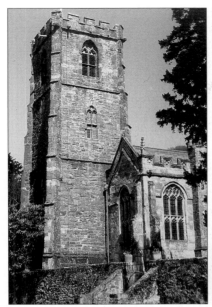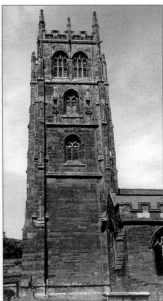

Fig. 83: The churches of west Somerset, such as these fine towers at Crowcombe (left) and Bishops Lydeard (right – photograph courtesy of Mick Aston)

bright red soils to remind you of the underlying geology. This colour is a characteristic of the vale, and indeed of west Somerset, and always gives away the presence of these Triassic rocks. It owes its origin to the arid climate in which the rocks were deposited and which caused the iron to be highly oxidised in the form of the mineral Haematite.

For all their interest, the Triassic rocks are poorly exposed in the vale and it is far easier to study them on the coast where they are well displayed. The lowest pebble beds are not seen on the north coast, but there is plenty of excellent exposure of Triassic sandstones and mudstones at a number of localities. The sequence at Watchet is described in the chapter which deals with this coast specifically, but it is worth discussing a few details of the Triassic rocks here.

Reconstructing the ancient Triassic environment

Although the Triassic rocks in Britain are often called the 'New Red Sandstone', this name is not entirely appropriate in Somerset, where much of the rock seen is actually quite fine-grained and silty rather than sandy. It is, however, deservedly called red because the iron-staining of this unit of rock is always conspicuous. Incidentally, the name 'New Red' is given because the rocks are younger than those of the Devonian period which have a somewhat similar appearance and are known as the 'Old Red Sandstone'. These rocks are dealt with in the chapters on the Quantocks, Brendons and Exmoor, and on the coast around Portishead and Clevedon. The dominant red colour is taken to indicate that the environment at the time of deposition of the rocks was very dry and you see a similar colour in many rocks and sediments after they have been baked, for example, in bricks and terra-cotta ware and in stones which have been heated after they have been burnt in a hearth. The colour is again due to the oxidised compound of Iron, Haematite. The presence of this mineral helps to explain something of the environment in the Triassic period, not that it was literally burning hot, but that it was very dry.

When we look at the rocks from this period we are studying an ancient desert environment in which water was very scarce. The rocks seen in Somerset include the basal pebble-beds mentioned above, and these clearly needed water for their transport, but today, even in the driest desert, rain does indeed fall. It often falls in rare storms and then the run-off causes floods which wash away the surface dust and sand. These become muddy torrents which can carry large boulders with them, which are ground together and rounded as they travel in the turbulent waters. The resulting deposits are therefore mixtures of pebble-beds and sandstones, with finer-grained muds in between representing the quieter periods after the flood waters calmed down.

The transition from land to sea

After these turbulent deposits, we find that higher beds in the Triassic period are dominated by rather finer-grained accumulations of silt and mud and these are the most common Triassic sediments in much of Somerset, especially on the north coast. Here the red colour remains to remind us of the arid climate, but the silts are well-bedded and towards the top of the sequence they show an increase in pale green/blue bands which marks the beginning of the influx of water into the environment. These bands are often associated with thin beds of sand, which was carried into the area by gentle currents of water as the silts were overwhelmed by the advancing sea. In the pale bands it is not unusual to find small burrows which penetrate down into the red silts below them, showing that animals were also able to colonise these shallow-water pools and that there was life in the area. The submergence of the area under the sea was only accomplished gradually and there were numerous episodes of dehydration following the water's advance, so that many of the sediments show evidence of shrinkage cracks on the their upper surfaces. These are seen as polygonal patterns in the sandstones and silts and are often accompanied by ripple-marks caused by wave action in the shallow pools (Fig. 82).

When, in this arid climate, substantial bodies of water were evaporated, they left behind all their dissolved salt and this was deposited in the sediment. Today we do not find salt crystals at the ground surface for the simple reason that in our climate they would dissolve away in a matter of weeks, so that they never reach the weathered surface of the ground. We do find crystals of another mineral called Gypsum, composed of Calcium sulphate, and this is commonly seen in the area round Watchet and in particular at Blue Anchor, as described in the chapter on these localities. Inland, near Puriton, there was once a salt extraction industry which pumped brine from these same Triassic rocks, showing that salt was indeed deposited in Somerset at this time. Further north, at Aust, on the shores of the Severn, it is still possible to find replicas of the salt crystals, preserved in a thin sandstone. These salt pseudomorphs and the presence of Gypsum, indicate quite clearly that sea-water was inundating the late Triassic shoreline.

Notable building stones

The vale of Taunton Deane meets the south-western side of the Quantocks where the villages of Bishops Lydeard and Crowcombe nestle in the shelter of the hills. Here we see some fine examples of architectural use of the local stone, notable amongst which are the church at Bishops Lydeard and Crowcombe Court (Fig. 83). Both display the excellent building qualities of the local red sandstones. Since this is an area where both New and Old Red Sandstones are to be found, not surprisingly, many of the buildings contain both types, and it is an interesting exercise to try to sort them out. In general, the New Red has the brighter red colour and although it is rather softer,

t is free from much natural weakness, and therefore better for carving into window mouldings etc. The Old Red is often more fissile, ie. it splits easily, but not necessarily along desired lines, so it is good for producing bulk walling material. This is often flaggy in appearance and has sharp edges. Sadly, many of the old quarries from which these stones were extracted have now been infilled, or lost under impenetrable growth of trees and scrub, and the New Red Sandstone quarries around Bishops Lydeard seem to have vanished. You will be able to see small local exposures of stone in lanes and streams though, and it is a pleasant area to explore.

Further east, the vale merges with the southern part of the Somerset levels and the rocks disappear under a cover of younger deposits, which will be described fully in the chapter on the levels. The vale of Taunton Deane is not notable for its exposures of rock but nevertheless has a strong geological influence on its topography, like the rest of Somerset, and would be of interest if only for this.

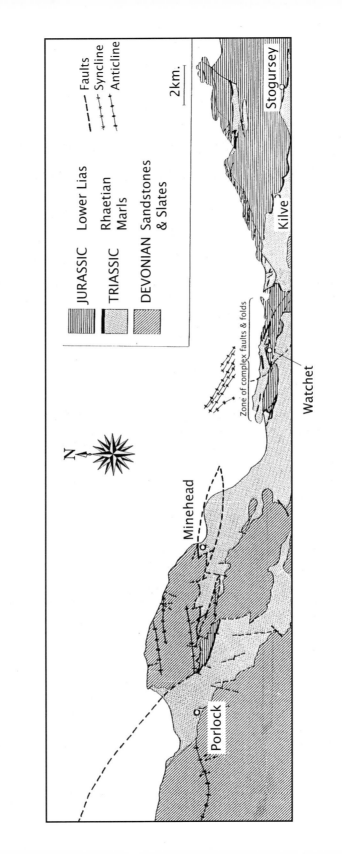

The Somerset Coast between Hinkley Point and Blue Anchor

The coast between Hinkley Point in Bridgwater Bay and Blue Anchor, near Minehead, has long been known to geologists for its superb exposures of the Rhaetian sediments (upper Triassic) and lower Jurassic rocks. These strata also occur throughout the low ground of central Somerset and form the foundations of the Somerset levels and the vale of Taunton Deane, but there are no really good inland exposures with the exception of a few quarries and even fewer natural ones such as the hill slopes of Hurcot Hill near Somerton. The best place to see them therefore, is on the coast (Fig. 84).

The geological feature of most interest is the sequence of rocks which spans the transition from the Triassic period, when Britain experienced an arid climate and was entirely dry land, to the Jurassic, when Britain gradually submerged under the sea. This sequence marks a very major event which brought to an end the dominance of land in much of Britain, a situation that had persisted since the Mendip Hills were created at the close of the Carboniferous period, about 295 million years ago. This high ground was only inundated after a substantial period of time but was eventually submerged completely in a process called marine transgression. On the Somerset coast there is no apparent break in the sequence of rocks that were deposited during this long period, which is unusual for a section that spans two major geological periods. Thanks to this continuity of deposition we can examine rocks which represent every detail of the marine transgression and see just how it was accomplished. During the Triassic period, sea covered much of the area which is now the land mass of Europe, but south-west Britain remained dry land until towards the end of the Triassic. The sea slowly advanced westwards to submerge the Somerset area and as it did so it brought with it marine animals. Plants began to colonise the land as the climate became less arid. There were several setbacks to the marine advance at first, largely due to small changes in the relative levels of land and sea.

Opposite, Fig. 84: The coast from Hinkley Point to Blue Anchor exposes a fine section through the late Triassic (Rhaetian) beds and into the lower Jurassic (Blue Lias). It is repeated by faulting at various places, and is affected by the major tear-faults which sweep through the coast along the NW/SE trend. (This map is a compilation from the British Geological Survey 1:50,000 Sheets 278 and 279).

Evolution in action, jerky or smooth?

If the land / sea levels were unstable it seems inevitable that there would be times when the newly flooded areas would dry out again. At other times, when there was sufficient water depth, animals would sweep in with the water to colonise new areas but when conditions changed, or the water retreated, the dead shells would be left to accumulate as fossils. If a significant period of time elapsed between such episodes, then the animals which next came along might well have evolved and changed slightly from their ancestors. This would then result in a band of fossils which would be recognisably different, ie a new species. When we examine these fossil bands today, we might very well conclude from the absence of intermediate forms that evolution always proceeds in substantial increments, large or small. If, however, we examined the fossil sequence in the sediments deposited in the main body of the sea where most of the evolutionary change took place, we might find an apparently continuous gradation between fossil species, with no distinctive breaks in the story. This would lead us to suppose that evolution proceeds by almost imperceptible change rather than by leaps and bounds. It is clear that in many exposures of rock there are time gaps in the sequence, large or small, and that we only see an incomplete record of the evolutionary changes that actually occurred. Thus, it is not surprising that many people have argued that evolution is in fact accomplished by a series of steps whilst others prefer the concept of gradual change. It has to be said that in the final analysis, any discernible change, no matter how small, might be regarded as a step, but some rare fossil sequences do show an almost imperceptible gradation between evolving forms of the 'same' species.

It may well be that this rather dry academic debate is no more than an argument about how much of the fossil record we can actually find. Due to the incompleteness of the record we often perceive that evolution is achieved by sudden changes from one species to another. This situation, and many others like it, demonstrate clearly the dangers of assuming too much from an incomplete geological record. If we attempt to use the absence of evidence to help 'prove' an argument or theory then the result is unlikely to be scientific truth.

The exposed geological sections on the Somerset coast are very long and will require several separate visits to be fully appreciated. They tend to be repetitive of the same sequence in places, but this is one of their attractions since we have an unusual opportunity to really get to know the rocks in great detail. The oldest rocks, the red sandstones and siltstones of the late Triassic, are seen in various places and amongst these the most interesting sections must include Blue Anchor and Watchet. At Blue Anchor we see the red rocks on the beach by the sea wall but if we walk a few hundred metres to the east, they are suddenly replaced by dark grey shales. This is due to a fault, which appears in the cliffs along this shore, and which drops the younger rocks on its eastern side. Beyond this fault the red rocks appear at a lower level on the shore where they can be seen to be overlain by the grey shale and limestone sequence seen in the cliffs (Fig. 85).

The transition from terrestrial desert to shallow sea-water was apparently interrupted at times because here we see clear evidence of the sea-water having been dried up by the heat of the sun. The salts which were dissolved in the sea-water were left behind in the sediment during this process and they are now to be found in the fossilised muds in the cliffs at Blue Anchor. Sea-water contains many salts of which common table salt, Sodium chloride, is only one. In addition to this there is an abundance of Calcium sulphate in the mineral form Gypsum. Gypsum is found in large nodular blocks lying on the beach at Blue Anchor and may be very attractively coloured salmon pink or orange, as well as pure white. It is a very soluble salt and in rain water it quite quickly dissolves to leave a deeply etched surface. On the beach the rapid mechanical erosion of the shingle is even more destructive of Gypsum and it assumes smooth and beautifully sculpted forms. It is almost impossible to visit Blue Anchor without carrying away a piece, I am obliged to admit! You will no doubt fall victim to the same temptation and I ask that you exercise a degree of restraint and satisfy your collectors instinct with a modest sample. There is plenty to go round, but for how many people and for how long? If, after a few years, your sample has languished in the garden and been subjected to rain rather than sea-water, you will no doubt observe that it has become rather rough surfaced and its exposed upper-side deeply pitted. This is due to the solution of the Gypsum by the rain water. It is remarkable how rapidly this happens, a few years will remove several millimetres. Consider this and then think that this Gypsum was crystallised 200 million years ago, and until you took it home it had not been significantly eroded! Humbling, isn't it? (Fig. 86).

Whilst at Blue Anchor you should also observe the sequence of rocks exposed on the shore under the high cliffs, which effectively mark the end of the beach, but beware possible cliff-falls. They do occur and could be very dangerous. Here, on the shore, the red rocks merge with grey shales and you will perhaps come across a bed of sandstone which has the appearance of crazy paving, with infilled cracks in its upper surface. These form a network, dividing it into polygonal areas. This form of cracking is identical to that which you might today see in dried-up muds on a river bank or lake bed, and it was caused by the dehydration that followed the first marine inundations, which also caused the crystallisation of the Gypsum that was dissolved in the sea-water (Fig. 87).

Another feature of this section which makes it famous in geological circles, is a bed of sandstone which has within it teeth, scales and bones of marine vertebrates. Amongst these there were many fish and also some marine reptiles, including crocodiles and the Triassic reptilian equivalent of modern mammalian dolphins, known as Ichthyosaurs. You will surely see these fossils but unless you look closely at them you may not realise it! They are small and it is necessary to get down on hands and knees and peer closely at the rocks to see them clearly. Don't expect to stumble over the odd skull or vertebral column on the beach, but do look for the scales and teeth, even though they are often only a few millimetres long. The way to find them is simple; just walk to the headland at the end of the cliffs and look for blocks of rock which look rusty. These are close to the many fallen blocks of pink and white Gypsum, so you will have to decide which to examine first. When you find a rusty looking block, look very closely. The small brown or black gritty things are mostly either teeth or scales of fish and reptiles, unless of course they happen to be blobs of crude oil from a tanker. This may seem far-fetched (the teeth and scales that is), but it's true. The rocks which contain these fossilised vertebrate remains are sandstones in which many of the sand grains are in fact fossils. In these sediments there was once an abundance of organic material and as it decayed this influenced the chemistry of the sediment. Its main effect was to cause the iron in the environment, from which most of the oxygen had been used up due to bacterial action, to be precipitated as minute crystals of iron sulphide. Originally this was black in appearance (this is why most muds are black under their surface layer), but in time it recrystallised to form the much more attractive golden-yellow and metallic-looking 'Fools Gold', properly called Iron Pyrites. The fresh and unweathered sediment is dark grey or black due to the presence of unaltered iron sulphide but after weathering it produces rusty coloured iron hydroxide compounds. Because of these chemical changes, the fossil-rich sediments often look a rusty brown colour and can be recognised from a distance (Fig. 88).

When you have finished with the mineral and fossil collecting at Blue Anchor, you should not leave before you have examined the cliffs in the headland, unless, of course, the tide is rising round your ankles. (By the way, you are unlikely to be drowned here, but may get very wet trying to regain the slipway to the beach when the tide is rising, so be very wary!) These cliffs demonstrate very clearly the effects of structural deformations that happened after the sediments were deposited. The cracks that resulted, known perversely by geologists as joints, are still present in the rocks, and are picked out by veins of Gypsum, which shows up clearly as white bands in the black shales. These Gypsum-filled cracks are clearly in two main sets, at oblique angles to the main bedding planes. They were all caused by the same force, because the stress on the rock produced pairs of fractures at angles which were complementary to one another. Such paired sets of joints are called 'conjugate', if you wish to impress your friends.

Mention of joints evokes memories of a visit to the coast between Lilstock and Kilve. The purpose of the exercise (of which there is plenty, since it is a round trip of about five or six miles), was to study the lower Jurassic rocks which are very well exposed along this section. The reason why the walk was so memorable was that nowhere have I seen better examples of jointing in sediments than on this section. If there was no other purpose to a visit than to study this one phenomenon, I should suggest this as the ideal locality. At one particular place the jointing is so regular as to suggest a wall, laid on its side, with blocks of limestone fitting together in apparently pre-determined patterns. In other beds the joints are less regular, but they all speak of immense forces acting upon the solid rock. The forces involved are trivial by comparison with those operating elsewhere in the Earth's crust, but by our human scale it all seems very impressive (Fig. 89).

The beds of rock in which the jointing is most conspicuous are limestones, and these are prominent in the lowest beds of the Jurassic system, which followed the Triassic. Rocks of this period, which commenced around 200 million years ago, are well known from many exposures in Somerset and Dorset, and outcrop in a belt which crosses the country to emerge on the Yorkshire coast. Although the rocks are exposed inland, they often form low ground because they are dominated by thick beds of clay. Many areas of Somerset, such as Taunton Deane and much of the Somerset Levels, are the result of erosion of clays and limestones of this age. The coast offers the best exposures, due to the rapid erosion of the cliffs by the sea, and on the shores there are wide flat ledges where the rocks can be easily studied (Fig.90).

Tide and time wait for no geologist!

The shores are backed by cliffs of varying height and there are several places from which there is simply no escape if the tide is high. For this reason no remote section, nor rock ledges near low water, should be visited unless the tide is falling and not about to turn. In any case you must get well clear of any cliff-backed sections, or any high ledges well out on the beach (such as occur at Hinkley Point and Watchet), when the tide turns at low water. **Please do not take any chances with the tides on this coast.** They are the second highest in the world and at full Spring Tide the rate of rise can be at least one inch every minute, or putting it another way, over your wellies in the time it takes to walk across a few hundred yards of slippery rocks! Talking of wellies, do not be tempted out on the beaches in the usual walking shoes, or worse still in trainers, not unless you like wet feet and ruined shoes, that is. The beaches are full of deep pools of water and often covered by banks of sticky Severn mud, and Wellington boots with good gripping soles are the only sensible footwear.

Having ventured out on to the beaches you will find that there is a vast expanse of rock exposed in many places. Good access is available at Hinkley Point, Lilstock, Kilve, St. Audrie's Bay, Doniford Bay, Watchet and Blue Anchor, and between these you have enough material to occupy a whole week of favourable tides. If you make several visits you will quickly get used to the main themes in the rocks, that is, the alternation of shales and limestones, the variation in depth of colour in the shales from black to pale grey, the presence of bright red silts and muds with accompanying sandstones in place of limestones, and in some localities, but not everywhere, abundant fossils.

The sequence in which these different types of rock occur is quite straightforward, although there is a lot of detail to interest the thoughtful observer. The general trend is to pass from red and pale grey/green marls at the base, through dark grey and black shales with a few pale grey limestones and buff sandstones, into a series of medium grey shales and paler grey limestones at the top. This trend towards limestone and away from sandstone shows that, as time wore on, the source of sand was diminishing, and that the sea was becoming more distant from any rivers which once supplied terrestrial sediment. During the later stages, the only land-derived sediment that arrived as particles suspended in the water was mud, and this settled out rather slowly to give the darker grey shales. At times the mud was diluted by lime, which precipitated from the sea-water, probably under the influence of the warm climate and low rainfall. This lime was also in the form of mud-sized particles and added to the general gloop on the sea-bed. Unlike the ordinary mud though, it soon began to set hard and the lime-rich sediment was never compacted and flattened out like the mud derived solely from the land. Thus, after some time, the limestones became cement-like, but the shales were compressed, losing their substantial water content. The fossils which were contained in them suffered the same fate; those in the muds were crushed flat, often to no more than about 5% or 10% of their original thickness, whilst those in the limestones are often apparently more or less as they were in life.

The fossils, for which this coast has become very well-known, were formed in the shallow waters of a warm sea, after it became sufficiently open to allow access to a variety of marine organisms. The earliest incursions of the sea produced nothing more than shallow salt-pans, in which few animals could live, and the only shells seen at first are those of small bivalves such as mussels and scallops. Far to the north there were extensive shallow lagoonal flats in which only algae could thrive and reference to the section on the Chew Valley will give you some idea of what these conditions must have been like. In most of the sections in the Watchet area you can find some examples of these early salt-tolerant faunas, in which the shells are very often extremely numerous,

Above, Fig. 85: The cliffs at Blue Anchor are cut by normal faults which juxtapose beds from the late Triassic with those of the lower Jurassic.

Below, Fig. 86: The late Triassic beds at Blue Anchor are crowded with nodular masses of Gypsum (Calcium sulphate) which formed during evaporation of the sea-water which deposited them.

Left, Fig. 87: The latest beds of the Triassic at Blue Anchor show sun-cracks, caused by dehydration after they had been exposed to the air.

Below, Fig. 88: The Rhaetian sediments at Blue Anchor include 'Bone Beds' which are full of the teeth, scales and bones of fish and reptiles.

Above, Fig. 89: The harder limestones of the Jurassic are heavily jointed by regional stresses all along the shore of the Bristol Channel, as here at Lilstock.

Below, Fig. 90: When the tide is low the beach shows a complex pattern of ridges of harder rocks in the late Triassic and early Jurassic transition.

Above, Fig 91: These scallop-like bivalves are in thinly-bedded black shales of the Rhaetian at Doniford Bay.

Below, Fig 92: Rhaetian fossils such as these bivalves *(Protocardia rhaetica)* are usually crowded together in densely packed bands.

Above, Fig. 93: The late Triassic marls which are usually red coloured are inter-bedded with pale grey bands which mark the incursion of water from time to time.

Below, Fig. 94: On the shores at Doniford Bay there are areas of late Triassic sandstone with well developed oscillatory ripple marks which were formed in shallow waters as the sea covered the submerging land.

Above, Fig. 95: Psiloceras planorbis is the first ammonite to appear in Britain, and marks the official start of the Jurassic period. It is common at Doniford Bay and elsewhere on the Somerset coast.

Below, Fig. 96: The second ammonite to be found in the British Jurassic rocks is *Caloceras johnstoni*, which is preserved in its original 'mother-of-pearl' colours.

Above, Fig. 97: Dapedius politum was a heavily armoured fish which lived in the muddy waters of the lower Jurassic sea. This specimen was found at Hinkley Point.

Below, Fig. 98: Amongst the early Jurassic fossils there are numerous spines of tiny sea-urchins. This one is preserved intact, and altogether is only 2 cm across!

Above, Fig. 99: There were so many ammonites drifting around in the early Jurassic seas that they sometimes became trapped against each other as they were swept along by the weak currents.

Below, Fig. 100: The ammonite shells were sometimes exposed at the sediment surface long enough for oysters and encrusting worms to colonise them. In some cases the oysters became moulded to the shape of the ammonite.

Above, Fig. 101: Coroniceras was an ammonite which grew to a large size, this one from Doniford Bay was around half a metre across.

Below, Fig. 102: The first ammonites found in the Jurassic rocks are possibly descended from each other and show evolutionary changes in form as illustrated by *Psiloceras planorbis* (the earlier smooth shelled form)and *Caloceras johnstoni* (weakly ribbed). This strongly ribbed ammonite is a much later form called *Arnioceras.*

Above, Fig. 103: The faulting and folding, as seen on the shore at Doniford Bay, was so intense that some strata now dip vertically.

crowding each other for space in the rock and even building up layer after layer of shell, with little sediment in between. Conversely, in all the sections you will see many beds of rock which, although they look perfectly suitable for fossils, are apparently totally barren. This must be due to the hostile nature of the environment during their deposition, but whether due to high salt content or lack of Oxygen, perhaps brought about by high temperature, or to other factors, is not clear (Figs. 91 & 92).

A note about fossil collecting

Many visitors to the coast will be delighted to find some very attractive fossils, in apparently inexhaustible supply in some places. Sadly, today it is often the case that fossils used to be numerous but now they are very much reduced. Few of us who have visited these fossil localities can honestly claim never to have removed fossils from the shore, but over decades of this steady but restrained collecting it was apparent that there were plenty to go round and many more left to be seen by others. In practice the sea removed far more by natural erosion than all the collectors put together. This was true right up until the early 1970's, when I first started to visit the shore and to collect specimens. In those days I often found the same individual fossils time and time again over several years and could even pick out the odd hole where I had collected a fossil, perhaps a couple of years before. However, after repeat visits over many years, it became obvious that the erosion of rock by the sea quickly rounded off and removed altogether the traces of my activities. In fact, within about five or ten years all these marks had gone, showing that erosion was moving perhaps 1 millimetre of rock per annum in places, so I comfort myself that the specimens that I collected in 1970-1980 would by now all have been lost to erosion if I, or someone else, had not taken them. On the other hand, the dramatic increase in public awareness of fossil and mineral collecting in the 1980's has caused some of these specimens to acquire a cash value and commercial collectors have started to dig them out using crow-bars, sledge hammers and even portable power tools. The result is that in some places a half metre or more height of rock has gone, and it would have taken maybe 500 years to wear the beach down to that level. In other words, nobody else will have the privilege of seeing that horizon exposed as it was a decade ago until the year 2500 at least! (And this assumes that nobody else will have a go until then.) So...if you want to collect fossils, do keep in mind that you are not alone, and that others will gain as much pleasure and interest from them as you do, if you leave them. There are now local bye-laws which prohibit attacking the cliffs and shore in some areas (in any case you should not hammer under cliffs for obvious reasons of safety), and remember that private land is not yours for the taking without permission.

Having collected your specimens, what then? Will you put them in an old shoe box in the garage, a polythene bag in the garden shed, or maybe on the mantelpiece? I hope that whatever their fate you will assume complete responsibility for them, after all they took 200 million years to get to you, the least you can do is to spend the next century looking after them! The sad fact is that the vast majority of the fossils collected probably end up rotting away in someone's back garden, where the elements are just as destructive as those on the shore, and where there is less chance of any educational value being attached to them. The moral message is clear, you must look after them, label them with their location and keep them dry and clean, ideally in a neat cabinet or some other safe place. Then, when you feel the urge to become a fossil yourself, you should make arrangements for them all to be donated to a local School, Museum or University, where they can be sorted out and used. Of all the really well cared-for collections that I have seen in my time, only one has been properly handed on to a reputable institution by the owner. I don't like to think of what the relatives will do to the many other collections, for which no such plans are made.

Well, enough of the discouraging warnings. In the hope that you will be a model student I can let you in to the secrets of where to see some really good fossils. The different sections tend to repeat the parts of the same sequence along the shore, but in varying proportions. This means that you might find similar species at many of them, but each locality usually displays one or more species better than anywhere else.

Perhaps the most complete sequence, with the best exposures, is that to be seen in Doniford Bay, east of Watchet. It is an extensive area, with ledges several hundreds of metres wide at low water spring tides, and it will take more than one tide to see all of them. I would suggest that you could make a start by walking to the headland overlooking the bay, by taking the harbourside path past the railway line, close to Watchet station, cross the field for about 500 metres to the far end, and descend the steps to the beach. If you observe the rocks in the end of the cliff you will notice that they are bright red, with occasional pale grey or buff bands. These are the last of the terrestrially deposited silts, and show the first signs, in the grey and buff bands, of the advancing sea (Fig. 93). Walk a little further, around the headland, and look at the ledges of harder rock before you. These are the buff sandstones of the salt water lagoons and in them you can see polygonal cracks where they were occasionally dried out when the water retreated. Ripple-marks due to shallow water wave action can also be seen on the top surfaces of some of them (Fig. 94). Nearby, and leading further out towards the sea, you will find a gully, with a constant stream of water which is draining from the higher part of the beach. If you follow it about two hundred metres, in your wellies of course, you will find yourself approaching a wide, flat area which is often occupied by some thick mud banks, sometimes as much as a welly deep! Steer round these but try to see the rocks in the area because they contain shells from the earliest marine episodes, which are still part of the late Triassic. These shells include forms such as mussels, scallops and other small bivalves. Very often the slabs of loose rock are literally covered by shells of one type or another. Carry on seawards and climb over the low ledges of limestone which begin to bar your path. The first few of these are without any conspicuous fossils. These beds are the last of the Triassic period. When you first notice an ammonite, looking like a flattened snail, you are (by convention) in the Jurassic period, and the fun is about to start! Once you have found the first occasional specimens the bedding planes quickly become covered in fossils and the more that you search along them the more you will see (Fig. 95). This is where the professional collectors get excited too, for amongst the beds of shale there is one at least where the ammonites are preserved with the most beautiful colours imaginable, looking rather like butterflies, with shining iridescent greens and reds. You might very well find one or two lying around loose but as likely as not they'll be incomplete. The reason is that the professionals cannot sell them, and prefer to take only whole ones. You may also see a mound of freshly-shattered rocks in a long line; this is where they have dug up tons of fresh rock in their search for the best specimens. Much of the rock is simply left where it fell, so you might be lucky and find a few that they missed as time weathers it away. I do hope so (Fig. 96). Many of the best fossils are found quite by chance. A beautiful fossil fish, *Dapedius politum*, came my way as I walked over the shore at Hinkley Point (Fig. 97).

When you have seen enough of the ammonites for which this area is justly famous, you might note that there are other less dramatic fossils about. If the day is warm and the sun is out, you could try getting down on your stomach on the flatter slabs of limestone and with a hand-lens and examine it in detail. With luck you will see oysters and other small shells. Closer observation may reveal black shiny discs, about 1 centimetre across, which are the jaw apparatus of the ammonites. Those with extremely sharp eyes and who do not mind pressing their noses to the rock, might see the very fine pin-like spines which once belonged to sea-urchins. These animals can very occasionally be found whole, with all their spines still arranged around the body (Fig. 98). The presence of these tiny fossils, and their very delicate preservation, shows that strong water-currents, and maybe even substantial waves, were totally absent in this area at the time of deposition of some beds of rock. Then again, on other bedding planes you might come across rows of ammonite shells which are stacked up just as dishes on a draining-board might be. The reason for this curious phenomenon is that at times there were very steady currents, and that these swept the empty ammonite shells along close to the sea-bed until one of them became stuck. Those which followed were either lodged against it on the upstream side, or by-passed it and went on their way. The result is a series of rows of fossils which are orientated parallel with the current, and in which every shell overlaps its neighbour in sequence. You can almost hear the echo of a gentle bump, as the shells clinked together for the last time! Fascinating! (Fig. 99).

Relatively common fossils, but easily overlooked, are the small worm tubes which encrust the ammonite shells. They are a chalky white and show up well on the coloured ammonites, where they are can be seen as small coiled marks, looking suspiciously like a small bird's dropping! Another fossil which colonised the hard shells of ammonites is the oyster which often mimics their shape, as it had a very thin shell on the side attached to the ammonite. These two common encrusting fossils demonstrate that after their death, the ammonites were frequently lying around on the sediment for some time before they were buried and this suggests that the sediments were accumulated very slowly. It also shows that the waters just above the sea-bed were sufficiently well oxygenated for bottom dwelling animals to live there (Fig. 100).

Evolution in the ammonites

'Slow but steady' might be the motto for the lower Jurassic, for although the sediment was clearly the product of a long period of gentle accumulation, the fossils which it preserves were nevertheless getting on with life and gently evolving, so that in successive beds we find slightly changed species. The earliest ammonites are seen to have very smooth plain shells, with no ornament, a species known as *Psiloceras planorbis*. The next level, some metres higher in the sequence, shows similar shells with a slight radial undulation or rib. These are known as *Caloceras johnsoni*, and look as if they were descended from *Psiloceras*. Higher up again in the sequence we see different ammonites, not necessarily direct descendants of the previous ones, with sharply developed ribs running all the way across the shell (Fig. 102). These changes in outward ornament are simple enough, but for the ammonites they represent a complete change of genera and species, just as big in its own way as that from early man to us, and of course, an enormous length of time, possibly greater than the entire history of the human race. These changes in ammonite shells were only the beginning in Britain, and the ammonites went on to develop into many beautiful, and some weird, shapes and ornamental forms, and we can now see in their evolution a story of never-ending change and diversification which all started, in Britain at least, in Watchet. You can follow this story later on in the chapter which includes the Ilminster area.

Fossils used for dating rocks

The evolution of the ammonites is of great importance to geologists because they can tell by looking at the ammonites in the rocks exactly which stratigraphic level they are in. This may seem trivial, but this form of age determination, using characteristic fossils, was at one time the only way to determine the age of the rock, and even now is the most precise dating technique we have for the relative ages of rocks. To those of us without a radiometric laboratory in the garage, it is still the only way to give an age to any rock. A systematic record of the various 'zone fossils' seen in all the horizons of rock throughout the country, and later the entire world, was slowly compiled over the last two centuries by many workers. As it happens, Britain was home to many early geologists, so we have in our own fossil record some of the worlds 'Type' localities for fossils from this sequence, and Watchet is one of them! *Psiloceras planorbis* was first recorded from here, and this remains forever its first scientific home.

Another rather overlooked aspect, is that in these constantly changing fossils we have abundant evidence for the frailty of species and the transient nature of their existence. It is true to say that no species has remained unchanged over geological time and that the vast majority have become extinct in a few tens or hundreds of thousands of years. It should be apparent from this, although there may not be much to be done about it, that the human species is no more likely to live forever than any other. When you wander around the beaches of the north Somerset coast you might well ponder some of these points as you observe the rocks. It is rare to make ten yards progress without seeing something worth the time it takes to get down and look, and the temptation to walk with fixed gaze for the next headland or ledge of rock should be resisted, unless the tide is after you of course! Take your time, observe closely, and don't leave until you have chewed over all the possibilities to explain what you see. You'll find yourself returning time and time again if you do, otherwise you'll have 'done' the coast in a day.

Structural features which affect the scenery

Whilst it is the fossils and the sediments that are the most obvious feature to draw visitors, another equally important one that should perhaps be emphasised is the geological structure, since this helps to explain not only what happened locally, but goes a long way to assisting our understanding of the geology of southern Britain.

The rocks on the coast are for the main part laid down in flat beds which even today are not too far from the horizontal, usually dipping fairly gently, often to the north. There are many places on the coast where this is not the case though. In some extreme examples, the dip of the beds can be seen to vary from horizontal to vertical over a few metres! More commonly, we find beds of sediment which follow curving lines of outcrop on the beach, indicating that they are folded and sometimes it is easy to see that small areas of rock form enclosed basins or mounds, due again to folding. Very often these gentle structural effects are associated with faults, which mark the point at which the strain on the rocks was just too great, and where they sheared due to mechanical failure. The essential feature of faulting is the separation of the once-adjacent sides of a fracture. In the case of the fault which cuts through Doniford Bay, at the steps down which you walked on to the beach, over 200 metres of vertical displacement occurred! The result of such dramatic faults is that the lower red Triassic rocks are now found at the same level as the higher fossil-bearing Jurassic rocks, and in the cliffs of this coast there are several localities where such an extreme relationship can be seen, notable amongst them are the cliffs at Blue Anchor and East Quantockshead. The bright red rocks suddenly disappear and are replaced by dull grey shales and limestones (Fig. 103).

Most of the faults which you will see show the 'normal' type of movement, which indicates a stretching of the crust of the earth. There are some others however, which demonstrate that movement was not so much stretching as

135

shearing, and these are known as 'wrench' faults. There is a famous one which appears just to the west of Watchet Harbour. The usual trend of these wrench faults in southern Britain is from north-west to south-east, and there are many examples known outside Somerset, as well as those within the county. The sense of the movement is a clockwise or 'dextral' shift, ie. rocks on the east of the fault go south relative to those on the west of it. This gives the effect of a sliding northwards of the south-west peninsula of Britain and partly explains why the north Devon hills are projected into the Bristol Channel. This dominant line of weakness in the rocks of the region is reflected in the course of some rivers, and it is partly responsible for the western edge of the Quantock escarpment and other similarly orientated features. There is also evidence for very significant faulting along the west Somerset coast near Porlock, where thick Jurassic sediments occur just a kilometre or so off-shore from the high cliffs of Devonian sediments.

To conclude, the coast from Blue Anchor to Hinkley Point affords us with some excellent exposures of a variety of sediments, many of them containing well-preserved fossils, and also offering some very peaceful and attractive walks. If you can manage a few hours on any stretch of this coastline you will surely find the geology well repays your close attention.

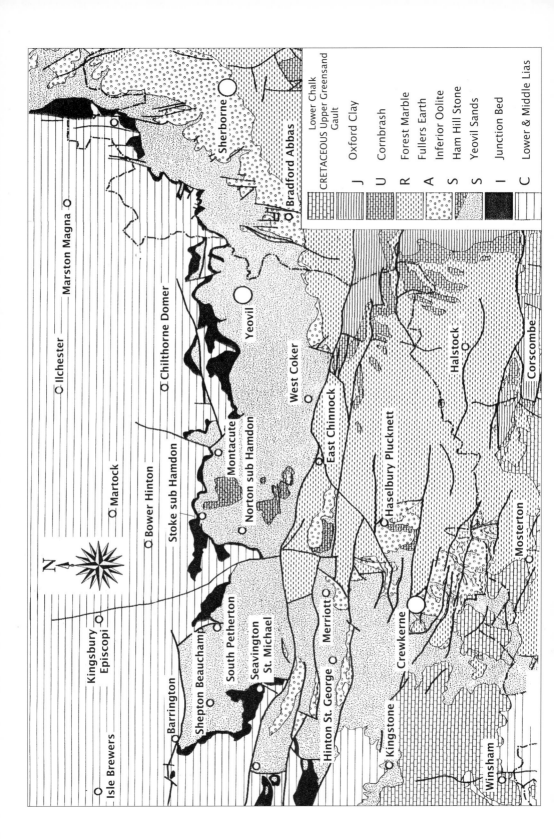

N

CRETACEOUS Lower Chalk
Upper Greensand
Gault

J — Oxford Clay
U — Cornbrash
R — Forest Marble
A — Fullers Earth
S — Inferior Oolite
S — Ham Hill Stone
  — Yeovil Sands
I — Junction Bed
C — Lower & Middle Lias

Isle Brewers

Kingsbury
Episcopi

Marston Magna

Ilchester

Martock

Bower Hinton

Stoke sub Hamdon

Chilthorne Domer

Barrington

Shepton Beauchamp

South Petherton

Seavington
St. Michael

Merriott

Hinton St. George

Montacute

Norton sub Hamdon

Sherborne

Bradford Abbas

Yeovil

West Coker

East Chinnock

Haselbury Plucknett

Halstock

Crewkerne

Kingstone

Mosterton

Winsham

Corscombe

From Yeovil to Crewkerne

The south eastern corner of Somerset has a scenic character which is quite unique in the county and owes its distinctive appearance to the variety of the local rocks which include many different beds of the lower and middle Jurassic period, ie. from around 190 to 170 million years old. These rocks are a mixture of clays, silts and sands and include a number of important limestone horizons too. They were laid down in relatively thin beds and are quite extensively faulted into blocks. These individual rectangular chunks of rock were uplifted and dropped relative to one another, so that the harder bands produce small hills, whilst the softer ones form the valleys. Since the extent of any one type of rock is limited, the scenery is locally very variable, with undulating hills and valleys characterising the region. This landscape continues southwards into west Dorset and all the way south to the English Channel.

The earliest rocks of this area are those of the Middle Lias, at which period of time the area was covered by sea-water which appears to have been rather shallow. The sediments deposited were mainly sandy and contained a great many fossils, notable amongst these being belemnites, early relatives of the modern cuttlefish, and brachiopods which were shellfish living on the sea-bed. There were also ammonites swimming in the waters above the sea-bed, together with fish and marine reptiles. The area around Ilminster is well known for the fossil fish that came from here when small local quarries were active, and the excellence of their preservation has produced some remarkable fossils. Some very good specimens can be seen in the County Museum in Taunton. The beds from which the fish were found at Ilminster are now long lost under quarry infill, but other horizons with ammonites and other shellfish can still be seen in small exposures in the lanes around the town (Fig. 105).

One of the most famous of these horizons of rock is called the 'Junction Bed'. This name is descriptive of the fact that in this one bed of rubbly limestone can be found the junction between middle and upper Lias times. The fossils that are contained in it are very numerous, an indication that there was very little

Opposite, Fig. 104: This map is drawn from the British Geological Survey 1:63,360 Sheet 312. Note how the central region is strongly affected by east/west trending faults which swing round to a north/south orientation in the eastern part. This structural feature is largely responsible for the topography of this part of the county.

sediment actually being accumulated whilst time ticked by. The fossils are known from other parts of England too, but there they are separated by great thicknesses of sediment, showing that they actually belong to separate time zones. This suggests that the animals that lived in the waters where Ilminster is now, were slowly evolving whilst the local environment barely changed. The slowness of deposition of this limestone bed resulted in some of the earlier beds being eroded and fragments from them were later redeposited in the higher parts. Consequently there are early fossil types in the Junction Bed, mixed up with later layers of limestone and later types of fossil. This curious mix might seem confusing at first but it simply reflects the long period of time that elapsed during the deposition of the whole bed. It is also apparent that many of the fossils were re-worked after their initial burial and that they were washed around and broken up before being re-incorporated into the sediment. Thus, we often find fossils in this bed which are broken up, even before our feeble efforts to extract them in one piece. Frustrating as this is, at least you don't feel quite so guilty should you break one! (Fig. 106).

The richness of the fauna in the Junction Bed has marked it out for the attention of collectors, and whenever it is exposed by roadworks or excavations it attracts swarms. You will find many of the fossils from here on sale in local mineral shops but they can still easily be found whenever the rock is exposed, or even in the freshly ploughed fields, especially after rain has cleaned the surface a little. If you find yourself around Ilminster, the Junction Bed makes a very distinctive platform which virtually surrounds the town on the eastern and northern sides, and anywhere on that flat-topped hill you might find fossils in the fields. Please respect the owners rights and ask permission first though (Fig. 107).

The rock which usually follows the Junction Bed in this area is at first silty and then later sandy, and is named after the town or village nearest to where it is exposed, so in this case it is the Yeovil Sands. This bed of rock is well-known amongst geologists because of its diachronous nature, or in plain English, it is not a unit of rock which can be regarded as of one age. In fact the age of the unit decreases as it is followed south from Cheltenham (where it is known as Cotswold sands) through Bath (Midford sands) to south Somerset (Yeovil sands) and finally to the coast at Bridport, (Bridport sands). The sands are very well seen in many roadside cuttings. Some of these are almost naturally formed, certainly not deliberately cut by Man, because it is the lanes that have cut their own way down through the soft sands over the centuries. Some of these are now as much as ten or more metres below the natural ground level and in the sides of them you can see the sands exposed. The sands are remarkably uniform in appearance wherever you see them, and are fine-grained and of rich ochre/

Above, Fig. 105: The Ilminster area was once famous for the fossil fish which were found in the quarries working the middle Lias. This fine specimen of *Lepidotus elvensis,* almost half a metre long, is in the collection of the Bath Royal Literary and Scientific Institution to which thanks are due for permission to photograph it.

Below, Fig. 106: The Junction Bed is a thin rubbly limestone which combines the Middle and Upper Lias. It is crowded with fossils from both periods and they show many subtle variations of form. These three are the ammonites *Dactylioceras, Harpoceras* and *Hildoceras.*

Above, Fig. 107: The Junction Bed forms a flat-topped platform of low hills around the Ilminster area.

Left, Fig. 108: The Yeovil Sands form escarpments around Yeovil and where roads cross these they are cut through to depths of ten or more metres as here at Babylon Hill.

Above, Fig. 109: The Yeovil sands seen here at Babylon Hill are fine-grained and ochreous in colour, with occasional nodules of lime-cemented sand which project from the weathered face.

Left, Fig. 110: Ham Hill Stone is possibly the best known of all the building stones in Somerset, and is found throughout the south of the county, and beyond. It is characteristically striated by the cross-bedding seen here.

143

Left, Fig. 111:
The quarries on top of Ham Hill are still being worked.

Below, Fig.112: The Bath Axis is a positive structural feature which appears to run from well to the north of the county (even as far as the Malvern Hills perhaps) right through Somerset and Dorset to the coast at Bridport. It represents a ridge, over which shallow waters deposited coarse shell sands during the early Jurassic times.

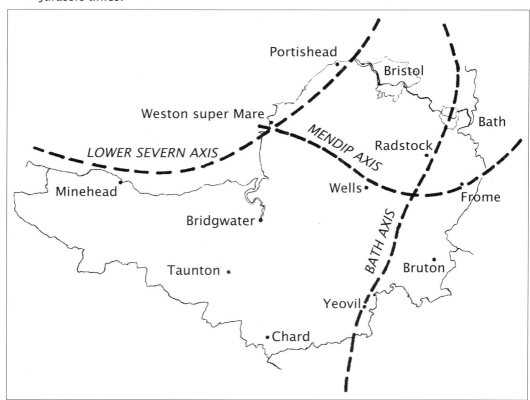

yellow colour. They usually exhibit occasional bands of harder nodules of lime-cemented sand which stand out from the sides of the banks, sometimes to the danger of passing cars. The sands are generally poor in fossils but when these have been found, they indicate an age which is variable depending upon which part of the outcrop they occur in. They are of Upper Lias age in this area. There is a discussion of the significance of the variable age of this bed in the chapter on Bath (Figs. 108 & 109).

The rocks which overlie the sands are rubbly limestone, which is known as the Inferior Oolite. The term suggests an indifferent quality but in fact means that the oolite is older than, and therefore below, the Great Oolite. In reality, it is inferior in quality, if building stone is what you require, but it still suffices very well for many local houses and you will see in most villages and towns in this area, a delightful combination of the three major stones, the middle Lias limestone, the Inferior Oolite and the Ham Stone from Ham Hill, near Yeovil. The middle Lias limestone and the Inferior Oolite give blocks of rough, fossil-rich limestone which can be worked into modest-sized blocks for normal walling purposes but which would be entirely inadequate for larger pieces such as lintels, sills, mullions etc. For these, the Ham Stone is preferred because of its excellent qualities as freestone (Fig. 110).

Ham Stone is a shelly limestone in which all the shells are broken up into small fragments. It appears that it was deposited on shell-banks which lay in a north/south belt . These lie in the vicinity of Yeovil, centred on Montacute, where the stone is found today. These fossilised shell-banks yield large blocks of mellow ochrous stone which can be carved readily into almost any shape or size. These qualities have established a ready market for the stone throughout the area from early historic times, and it can be seen in almost all the local buildings, whether church or mansion, and even in the humble cottages in the villages. The Ham stone was known to, and used by, the Romans, and is found in buildings of all ages. It was dug from deep quarries on Ham Hill and also on Chiseldon Hill nearby, but impressive as the old quarries are, it is still hard to imagine how so many buildings came out of one or two holes in the ground! (Fig. 111)

The environment from which the Ham Stone was deposited was evidently one in which there was a great deal of wave energy, for the shells which make the bulk of the rock were broken up into many tiny fragments. Despite its widespread use in buildings, there are very few exposures of the Ham Stone in the area, in fact they seem to be limited to Ham Hill and around Chiseldon, a nearby village, and are evidently associated with some local geological phenomenon because laterally (ie to east and west), the stone merges into the sands described above. The interpretation which most geologists accept is that the Ham Stone represents a narrow north/south orientated ridge where shelly banks accumulated due to the waves washing over a shallow bank. The sands on either side were presumably deposited in slightly quieter and deeper waters, without accumulations of shells.

The ridge over which the sands were deposited is an important feature of the geology of southern England. It can be detected everywhere between the Malvern Hills in Worcestershire and the coast in Dorset. This feature in the ancient land/seascape is of such enduring importance in the geological record that it has to be one of the major influences on the deposition of rocks in southern England. It stretches for a hundred miles or more, from the midlands to the Channel, and is clearly a persistent structural unit throughout geological time, at least for the last 500 million years! It is likely that the Malvern Hills and even the Longmynd and Wrekin in Shropshire, are all connected with it, and the north/south structures continue even further into the north of England in the form of faults and folds. It is now difficult to unravel the complex history of the sequence which overlies the ancient structural basement of the earth's crust in England but we can begin to appreciate that the foundations of our Somerset geology are linked with some of the most ancient rocks in the country (Fig. 112).

Following the deposition of sands and limestone in the middle Jurassic, there was a prolonged period of clay deposition which left a vast thickness of shales and clays, with only intermittent sands and limestones. It started gently enough with the Fuller's Earth and associated Fuller's Earth Rock (a limestone), but soon after came the Forest Marble limestone, described in more detail in the section on east Somerset, and then the Oxford Clay. This thick unit of clay was punctuated by the Cornbrash, a thin sequence of shelly limestones which is well known, as its name implies, for the quality of the soils which it generates. The outcrops of Cornbrash have been widely employed for cereal growing and form light and easily cultivable ground on distinctive flat platforms. But these lie beyond the Yeovil area, a few miles to the north, and you need to see the Chapter on the eastern borders.

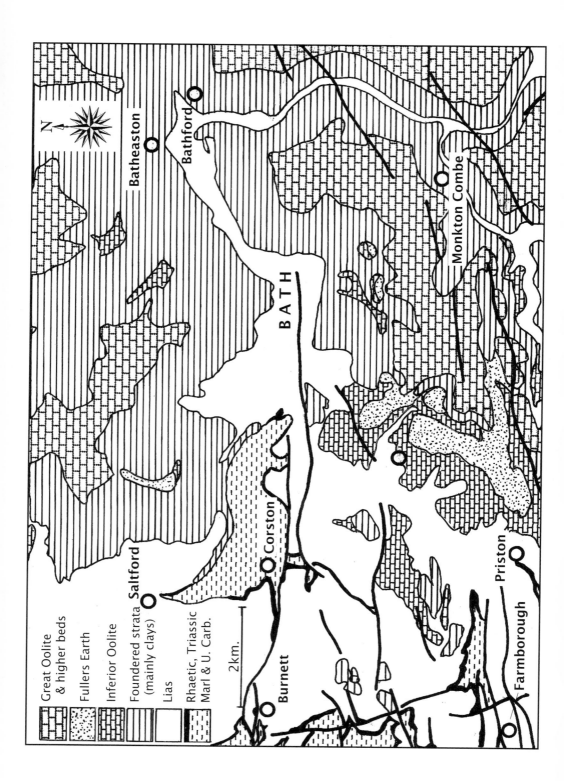

Legend:
- Great Oolite & higher beds
- Fullers Earth
- Inferior Oolite
- Foundered strata (mainly clays)
- Lias
- Rhaetic, Triassic Marl & U. Carb.

N

2km.

BATH

Batheaston
Bathford
Monkton Combe
Saltford
Corston
Burnett
Priston
Farmborough

Bath

The City of Bath lies in the valley of the River Avon where its course swings from northwards to westward (Fig. 114). It is at a crucial point in the geology of the area, marked by major structural features, which allow an upwelling of the famous hot springs which gave the city its name. The waters which rise to the surface at Bath were heated deep underground by the same heat which is present everywhere in the earth, but is normally barely perceptible at the surface. It is soon apparent underground however and 'cavers' will know that the normal temperature in a cave is around 10 degrees Celsius (50 degrees Fahrenheit), summer and winter. Miners, on the other hand, will tell of far higher temperatures as they go deeper underground, and in some British mines, for example in Cornwall, the working temperature reaches around 35 degrees Celsius. This heat, which was originally generated by radio-active elements decaying deep inside the earth, is capable of heating ground waters under pressure to temperatures well above their normal surface boiling point, so that in some regions of the earth the water suddenly turns into steam as it nears the surface. But here in genteel and restrained Bath it rises at a more moderate temperature below boiling point. The water itself is not derived from deep underground sources, but is recycled rainwater from the cooler overlying rocks, some believe that it started off in the Mendip Hills. Having seeped down deep into the ground it became heated and eventually returned to the surface by a process of convection. In its progress through the rocks the water dissolved some of their minerals, notably lime and other easily soluble substances. The resulting rather salty mixture is far from the original pure rainwater, but being 'natural' has been deemed by many to be 'good for you'. It can be sampled at the famous 'Pump Room' where you can decide for yourself whether you prefer your water ready-salted or plain!

Geological summary of the region

The geology of this region, which commences with the lower Lias, is dominated by a resistant cap of limestone. This surface cover of hard Jurassic rocks overlies

Opposite, Fig. 113: The region around Bath is dominated by flat-topped hills which are formed by the Great Oolite in the north and east, and the lower Jurassic beds to the west. (This map is drawn from the British Geological Survey 1:63,360 Sheet 265).

a sequence of soft shales, clays and sands. The limestones on the top of the hills are oolitic and are the source of the famous Bath Stone, used in all the finest buildings in the city. These oolitic building stones are still mined on a small scale, mostly in neighbouring Wiltshire, but were formerly dug on the high ground within sight of the city centre.

The area to the south of the city between Frome, Shepton Mallet and Bath is mostly high ground at around 130 metres O.D. It forms a relatively flat plateau which is cut by a few deep valleys, and there are a number of isolated and rounded hills which look very much like islands in a shallow sea, which is probably exactly what they once were. Notable amongst these are Stantonbury and Winsbury Hill at Marksbury and Priest Barrow and Farmborough Common close to Farmborough. Kelston Round Hill is another distinctive landmark of similar origin. On this elevated plateau, the earliest post-Carboniferous rocks are found. On the western side of this region these include some of the late Triassic sediments from the Rhaetic period and especially interesting amongst these are the pale creamy-grey limestones, which include the famous 'Cotham Marble'. This rock is better known from Cotham Hill in Bristol from where blocks of this algal limestone were commonly dug. The distinguishing feature of this particular bed of limestone is the beautifully preserved growths of fossil algae which look very much like miniature trees in vertical sections. The upper surface of these blocks of limestone was often hummocky due to the uneven development of the algal growths. Within the blocks finely laminated limestones are draped over these hummocks to give vertical sections an extraordinary resemblance to a rural scene, with hedgerows, trees and summer skies. If all this sounds a bit fanciful don't take my word for it but see for yourself in the plate (Figs. 115 & 116). There is a fuller discussion of this special stone in the Chapter on the Chew Valley.

The Rhaetic beds, which include this Cotham Marble horizon, are extensively preserved in the area just south west of Bath, around the village of Burnett. The fields here are often littered with blocks of pale creamy-white limestones, and many of the older buildings are made of the same stones which gave a very useful flat-bedded building block with relatively little effort required of the quarryman, other than to dig them up. The pale creamy-white colour is very typical of this horizon and gives it the common name of 'White Lias' which distinguishes it from the next and overlying series of rocks. This comprises darker blue/grey limestones and is known as the 'Blue Lias'. This blue colour may seem very obscure on an overcast day, but to an artist or a geologist deprived of many distinctive colours in his rocks, it is often very apparent, especially on a sunny day when the sky seems to be reflected in the rock (Fig. 117). The White Lias marks the transition from land to sea over a very wide area of Britain and is

Above, Fig. 114: Bath is sited in a deep valley cut by the River Avon through Jurassic rocks.

Below, Fig. 115: The plateau to the south west of Bath, e.g. around Burnett, are covered by the Rhaetic sediments amongst which this limestone, the Cotham Marble, is represented. The algal growths in the cross-section were formed in shallow saline lagoons.

Above, Fig. 116: When cut in vertical section the Cotham Marble shows remarkable tree-like growths which were formed by algae.

Below, Fig. 117: The typical building stones of the the area south of Bath are the White and Blue Lias limestones. Both have been used to build this wall.

Above, Fig. 118: In the Keynsham district especially there were many ammonites dug from quarries which worked the Blue Lias. These often found there way into buildings.

Below, Fig. 119: The rock which made Bath famous is an oolitic limestone from the Great Oolite horizon of the middle Jurassic.

Fig. 120: Unfortunately, the oolitic limestone of which most buildings in Bath are constructed is prone to frost attack and chemical damage by polluted air, so that many old buildings now show evidence of damage and repair. This is in the Royal Crescent.

Fig. 121: William Smith has been called 'the father of English geology'. He lived near Bath (at Tucking Mill) and drew the first geological maps ever made in this area.

Fig. 122: Despite the plaque which states to the contrary this attractive cottage (right) was apparently not William Smith's home! He is believed actually to have lived about 50 metres away in this solid property (above left).

Above, Fig. 123: The Midford Sands, which are very similar to the Yeovil Sands in appearance, are actually somewhat earlier, although they were deposited by the same shallow sea as it migrated across the region.

Below, Fig. 124: This diagram shows the diachronous horizon which is represented by the sands of the middle Lias. These are known from their local place of exposure, e.g. the Bridport Sands, Yeovil Sands, Midford Sands and Cotswold Sands.

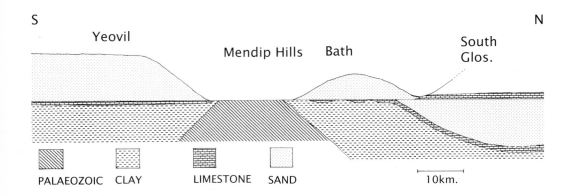

the end of an era in our geological history. A piece of this limestone represents a momentous event in the geological history of the region, the submergence of a land mass and its replacement by an ocean. This is discussed in detail in the chapter about the coast between Minehead and Bridgwater Bay.

The deepening sea effectively drowned the Mendips and the land to the north, well beyond Bath. The sea-bed at the time appears to have been at least approximately comparable to the modern topography so that in the north of the county the sea was very shallow for some time, whereas further south, beyond the Mendip Hills in central Somerset it may well have been some hundreds of feet deep. The sediments found in the northern shallow area are what you might expect from a modern shoreline region. They have coarse sand grains mixed up with the finer muds, the shelly debris is broken up and whole fossils are rather rare. The fossilised shells are quite numerous however and this is probably a reflection of the slow accumulation of sediment, caused by constant reworking and erosion of the finer particles. The heavy shells were washed around and broken up, whilst the tiny particles of mud could hardly settle. In quieter moments, the shell debris and sand was deposited, and some at least was preserved to form rock. The localities in which you can now find Lower Lias rocks exposed are not very many. In the 'good old days' of local quarrying it was easy to find outcrops in or around the villages, but now you will need sharp eyes and an even sharper machete to see more than the odd glimpse of rock peeping out from behind brambles, ivy and nettles in the old quarries. Although it is perhaps not very scientific, you can often study the rocks more easily in old walls and buildings than *in situ* and it is at least worth a look at old buildings to see if any fossils or other interesting features are visible, in particular the larger ammonites which were often incorporated into house facades. Please do not be tempted to remove any specimens from buildings or walls though! (Fig. 118).

Bath Stone

The stone from which Georgian Bath is built, is simply known as 'Bath Stone'. It is actually a series of beds from the formation known to geologists as the 'Great Oolite'. This is an oolitic limestone which appears slightly higher in the stratigraphic column than the Inferior Oolite. The term 'Great' is probably applied because in the Cotswolds this is the thicker of the limestones in many places, and the one first used for quarrying since it is on top! This stone was quarried and mined around Bath from early times, but it really became appreciated during the 18th Century when a local gentleman, Ralph Allen, opened extensive workings near to Bath on the high ground just east of the city. This area is just inside the old Somerset boundary and although most of the stone mines are in fact in Wiltshire, Somerset can claim to have within its bounds a source of perhaps the most famous building stone in Britain. The mines at Combe Down which supplied much of this stone are nowadays disused but, because of local subsidence, are causing considerable problems for the residents whose houses are built above them. Although Bath Stone is an admirable building stone its removal from within three or four metres of the ground surface has resulted in many instances of roof collapse in the mines. Unfortunately this collapse was not immediately after the mining and relatively modern houses were built above the mines before it became apparent, consequently there are now schemes to infill the mines in the hope of preventing one part of Bath sinking into the hole from which another part was created!

Bath stone is a form of limestone in which the grains are small spherical pellets called Ooliths, or Ooids, both meaning 'Egg stones'. Although sounding rather improbable, the comparison is between blocks of the fresh stone and lumps of fish roe, which when fresh and creamy-white, closely resemble each other in appearance if not in taste! (Fig. 119). The horizon of rock from which the Bath stone is quarried, the Great Oolite, is a major component of the Cotswold limestones. The modern stone mines are mostly situated in Wiltshire. Earlier ones were conveniently located on the hills immediately above the city. The stone was delivered down an inclined railway to within the city boundary, close to the canal at Widcombe, using gravity as the source of energy . It was the development of this industry which made the wealth of Ralph Allen. The property of the stone which made it so suitable for building was a combination of its availability in very large blocks, which allowed it to be easily worked into large masonry and its smooth and uniform texture, which made it ideal for carving into subtle shapes. Unfortunately the softness of its minerals which made it an almost ideal building stone was also its main weakness. It is neither mechanically nor chemically very strong, so much so that most of the original stones from 18th Century buildings show some signs of weathering, and many of the finer details have been lost to frost action and solution by rain water. In the last decades of the 20th Century, after over almost two centuries of industrial pollution, the last original columns from the colonnades outside the Pump Room have been lost, although it must be admitted the very last one succumbed to a car! (Fig. 120).

Although the Great Oolite is responsible for the massive Cotswold escarpment to the north of Bath, a few miles south of the city it has almost disappeared from the sequence altogether. In this area the limestone is replaced by clays and these become dominant over the limestone so that Bath Stone is not found there. These clays, which are best seen today around Bradford-on-Avon in Wiltshire, are also economically important, or at least they were in the past. Their importance lay in their properties of absorption, and they were dug in pits around Bradford-on-Avon and elsewhere, such as the heights of Odd Down just south of Bath, from where they were mined until well into the latter half of the 20th Century. The clay minerals are in fact very tiny crystals, with electrically charged surfaces which attract other molecules and so enable the clays to absorb considerable volumes of water, oils etc. This oil-retaining property was particularly useful in the process of de-greasing wool called 'Fulling' and the clays which were especially suitable became known as 'Fuller's Earth'. I write on this subject with mixed emotions for I once had a garden sited on Fuller's Earth and this substance makes very sticky soil indeed! Fuller's Earth was still mined commercially in Bath at Odd Down until the 1980's and was valued as a thixotropic agent in paints and as a filler in pharmaceuticals, amongst many other uses.

Somerset, the Home of geology!

Whilst writing of Bath I must make mention of the historic importance of the city in the study of geology. It was around Bath, as well as over much of England, that William Smith, the man often called 'The Father of English Geology', once travelled in his occupation as engineer and surveyor (Fig. 121). He was responsible for finding routes for the new canals which were being built across the country in the 18th Century and in this job he recognised that the rocks he encountered could be related to each other, and that their sequence was predictable. This stemmed from a childhood interest in collecting fossils. He found that the fossils from two separate rock bands were entirely different , thus becoming the first man to recognise the science of Stratigraphy, and incidentally proving that a misspent youth can be a good grounding for life! He mapped the areas in which he worked and produced the first comprehensive geological maps in the world. At one time he lived at Tucking Mill (Fig. 122), which lies inside the Somerset border by the merest whisker, on the northern bank of the Midford Brook at Monkton Combe, just below the famous stone mines of Combe Down. Thus, if William Smith is the 'Father of English Geology', then Somerset can fairly claim to be the 'Home of English Geology', can't it?

Midford, a tiny village which straddles the Somerset/Wiltshire border, has another claim to fame in addition to having been home to William Smith. It is the type locality for the 'Midford Sands' (Fig. 123). This may seem a rather less substantial claim, but these sands are well known to the British geological community, because they are a part of a fascinating story, often told in lectures and text-books, and twice in this one! (See the Chapter on Yeovil for the other version). The Midford Sands are also found in other places. In Yeovil they are known as the 'Yeovil Sands', in Bridport (Dorset) they are called the 'Bridport

Sands', and in Cheltenham, guess what they are called! No, they are the 'Cotswold Sands', but full marks for trying!

In all of these exposures the sands appear to be identical, in that the sediment itself is always a fine-grained, well sorted and ochrous yellow sandstone, with occasional bands of harder lime-cemented nodules. Where they differ is that they are not all exactly equivalent in terms of their age. Although the rocks themselves look identical, this appearance only reflects conditions during their deposition. The similarity of appearance does not mean that they are of the same age. In practice, it is fossils that give the best field evidence for the age of rocks, because they were constantly changing due to evolution and appear as unique time markers in the rocks. However, even fossil evidence is not an absolute time indicator, but it is far better evidence than the appearance (the lithology) of the rocks themselves. In this example the fossils which appear at the top of the sands in the north of the region are only found part-way up the sands in the south, and later forms appear in the south, which are totally absent from the sands in the north. This may be more easily understood by reference to the diagram (Fig. 124).

The significance of the sands, which appear everywhere on the line between Cheltenham and the south coast at Bridport, is that they are apparently identical in lithology (the fancy name for their mineral composition and texture) and yet they are known from their fossils to change in age as they are followed along the outcrop. In the north they are older than they are in the south. What does this mean in terms of a landscape, or seascape as this happens to be? The inference is that the sands themselves represent an environment that moved across the area with time. Thus, in the early stage, we see sands being deposited in the north and in the last stage it is the south coast where the sands are deposited. The sands were deposited in the intermediate areas sometime in between. Clearly the area around Bath was an unstable one during much of the Jurassic Period, with occasional emergent shoals. The sea was never very deep, and the waves must often have broken on the shallow lime sand-banks, effectively proving a barrier to marine life which enjoyed quiet waters further south. There is more discussion of the relationship between rock type and fossils in this bed in the chapter on the Yeovil area.

If you wish to see exposures of the Bath stone you can visit one of the underground mines which still operate, but these are outside the city, some in the Corsham area. There are some good exposures on the hills overlooking Bath however and you could go up to Brown's Folly, which is the hill just across the River Avon above Bathford village. There is an excellent booklet available, 'The Rocks of Brown's Folly' by R.B.J.Smith (published by the Bath Geological Society), which will guide you around this hill-top site, and within a couple of hours you can see a good selection of exposures to illustrate some of the properties of the local stone. Brown's Folly is the site of old stone mines too, so as you walk around you will be standing on top of some of the mines from which the city below you was built. There are also roadside exposures of Bath Stone up North Hill in the grounds of the University of Bath, which can easily be seen in a short drive from the city centre.

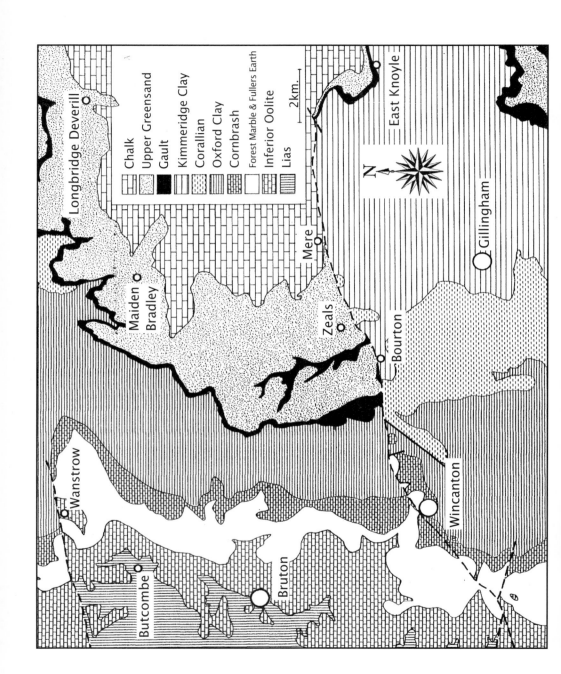

Chalk
Upper Greensand
Gault
Kimmeridge Clay
Corallian
Oxford Clay
Cornbrash
Forest Marble & Fullers Earth
Inferior Oolite
Lias

2km.

N

Longbridge Deverill

Maiden Bradley

Zeals

Mere

Bourton

East Knoyle

Gillingham

Wanstrow

Butcombe

Bruton

Wincanton

The Eastern Borders

From building stone to clay

The eastern borders of the county are marked by elevated land over much of their range and commence in the northern corner around Bath with the high ground above the city. This is formed from mid-Jurassic limestones of oolitic type. These beds are massive and strong enough to resist weathering and form flat-topped hills which extend northwards to become the Cotswolds. The best known of the rocks, the Great Oolite, has a maximum thickness of around 33 metres near to the city but just a few kilometres to the south it has been replaced entirely by clays. Just east of the city the flat-topped limestone hills are isolated by deep valleys cutting through the limestones into the soft sands and clays of the lower Jurassic Lias. Individual outcrops such as Bathampton Down and Claverton Down form the borders with Wiltshire. Further south the oolitic limestones are replaced in part by the Fullers Earth Clay, a soft deposit which was worked locally until very recently for use in industrial processes, but which is best known for its traditional use in wool treatment, and which made the beds commercially very valuable. The best clays were worked in mines and the last of these, on Odd Down just outside the city boundary, closed in the 1980's. (Fig. 126).

Forest Marble and Cornbrash

With the passing of the thick limestones the hills they supported are also lost, so that further south on the Somerset/Wiltshire border the scenery is rather less dramatic, with lower hills and flatter countryside marking the softer beds and thinner limestones of the Jurassic system. The harder limestones are principally comprised of two major formations in the mid-Jurassic; the lower being the Forest Marble, and the upper the Cornbrash. The Forest Marble is a composite unit of rocks totalling around 30 metres in thickness, with a hard limestone at its base and other sandy and limy beds throughout, but being mainly clay. It weathers to a flat-topped plateau and forms most of the country between Hinton

Opposite, Fig, 125: The Eastern borders of Somerset are typified by this area, drawn from the British Geological Survey 1:63,360 Sheet 297. Note that the highest Jurassic beds (i.e. the Kimmeridge Clay) do not appear north of the Mere Fault. This is because this fault was active around this time and none of these younger Jurassic sediments have been preserved on its northern side.

Charterhouse and Frome and outcrops over a north-south distance of about 15 kilometres. This plateau is about 10 kms wide from east to west which makes it a very substantial area of flat land. Above the Forest Marble there lies the Cornbrash which is a limestone of rubbly character. This has acquired its name because of its suitability for cereal growing due to its well-drained and fertile stony (brash) soils. It outcrops between Norton St. Philip, Woolverton and Rode and further south around Bruton, and so is only just seen in Somerset. The beds of Jurassic rock in this area, as in much of the county, are dipping very gently to the east, often at less than 5 degrees from the horizontal. The effect of this is to cause the plateau of rock to descend to the east so that the younger and higher beds of the Cornbrash, even though they rest on top of the Forest Marble, are at slightly lower topographic elevation (Fig. 127). Both the Forest Marble and the Cornbrash are noted for containing abundant fossils. If you get an opportunity to examine them in exposures, or even to look in ploughed fields, you may well find shells of brachiopods, bivalves and fragments of echinoderms and other marine fauna, together with bits of carbonised wood and more rarely, fish teeth. The Forest Marble is named from its once having been quarried in the forest of Wychwood in Oxfordshire, where it was worked and polished to reveal its rather attractive appearance, thus acquiring its erroneous descriptive name. It is not a true marble but an unmetamorphosed limestone.

Buried Palaeozoic foundations

Just south of Frome, a very substantial fault, the Marston Fault, drops the rocks to the south, bringing the higher beds of the Jurassic to outcrop against the Forest Marble. The next twenty kilometres of the Somerset/Wiltshire border is dominated by the heavily wooded Bruton Forest and the flat-lying Oxford Clay belt. This north-south orientated strip of countryside is very thinly populated, presumably due in part to the heavy clay soils. It is more or less coincident with the Somerset/Wiltshire border, suggesting that the geology has again controlled the political boundary in this region. A boggy and heavily-wooded area with low population presumably would be less likely to be argued or travelled over than one with high population density and fertile soils.

The major faults, such as the Marston Fault, which trend approximately east-west in this area, are apparently parallel to the structural axis of the Palaeozoic rocks seen in the east Mendip hills and it seems likely that these faults are being controlled by this older underlying geology. Even though these older rocks have been long lost to sight, their structures have been active more recently and affect far younger rocks. This demonstrates the longevity of some geological structural features, many of which can be shown to have been active over tens or even hundreds of millions of years.

The road from Evercreech to Bruton is a good example of the sudden change in topography that these higher mid-Jurassic rocks can impart on the landscape. It starts gently enough in the Lias clays of the lower Jurassic, winding along the country lanes towards the south east, but soon climbs steeply on to a high ridge, from where impressive views to the north and east reveal a much changed country. The green fields of rich grazing in the lowlands are replaced by more undulating land with a series of beds of harder rock forming escarpments. These include the Middle Lias limestones, the Inferior Oolite and the Fullers Earth Rock, all of which resist weathering and erosion better than the intervening clays and sands. Further eastwards still, the thin soils over the Forest Marble give grazing land on the high escarpment which starts just east from Bruton, from where the distant Greensand and Chalk escarpments can be glimpsed. Buzzards circling overhead give the region a wilder feel and very few buildings detract from the sense of isolation.

Turning northwards from Bruton, the A359 road to Wanstrow follows the escarpment of the Forest Marble for six kilometres of uninterrupted rural scenery, with the lower Jurassic sediments forming the low ground away to the west and the heavy Oxford Clay producing the heavy soils, which support the Bruton Forest, to the east. Behind this we see the heavily tree-covered escarpment of the Greensand on the skyline marking the edge of the Cretaceous rocks and the end of our county, because beyond the trees is Wiltshire. There are some old workings in the Forest Marble still visible adjacent to the road just a few kilometres north from Bruton, close to Gilcombe Farm (Figs. 128 & 129), and the Cornbrash, which rests on top of it, is re-worked in soils of the well drained fields on top of the dip slope, a kilometre or so to the east. You may also note some old lime-kilns around here indicating the nearby outcrops of limestone (Figs. 130, 131 & 132).

The Mere Fault

Towards the southern end of this Oxford clay belt is another substantial fault, again trending roughly east-west, this time running through Wincanton. It is known as the Mere fault, named from the striking topographic feature that it makes just over the Wiltshire border. This one downthrows to the north, although in its long history it has reversed its sense of movement and has been both a thrust fault and a normal one. This means that at times the crust has been squeezed and has overridden itself, and at others it has stretched out again on the same line. The effect of this fault is to break the north-south line of the escarpment of the rocks which we have been following, and to set back the outcrop of the lower Jurassic rocks by quite a few miles to the east.

The Vale of Wardour

This leads us into the Vale of Wardour, fascinating geologically for its inland exposures of the highest Jurassic Portland and Purbeck beds, but forbidden territory for Somerset geologists! Well, nobody's going to mind, so why not have a quick look whilst you're here? Head across the flat Kimmeridge Clays east of Gillingham for the area to the east of Tisbury and see the highest Jurassic limestones appearing near Chicksgrove. There is a quarry here in the Portland and Purbeck beds and the owner, at the time of writing, is very welcoming to genuinely interested visitors. If the quarry is closed you can still see examples of the local stone and its use in the beautiful farm buildings nearby and there are some large fossil ammonites from the Portland Stone built into the local cottages.

Greensand

If you have been tempted to make this excursion beyond the boundaries, you will notice that you are closely surrounded to north and south by high ground, with sharp escarpments rising from the low clay vale. These Cretaceous rocks are only just seen in the most eastern parts of Somerset, around Penselwood, where they form quite dramatic escarpments. The first of them is that of the Upper Greensand. This bed of rock is resting on a thick silty clay, the Gault clay, which causes the overlying beds to founder and collapse wherever the slope is steep enough. Consequently, there are substantial landslips on the edges of this escarpment, just west of Penselwood and also on the fault bounded southern edge of the Greensand, just south of the village. Further east, the lower Chalk outcrops at Mere but is not represented in Somerset.

The rocks of these parts of the county are, in general, poorly exposed although there are well hidden hollows cut into the Greensand escarpments by the wheels of long-forgotten waggons before the days of metalled roads. Sometimes these can be as much as forty feet below the surrounding land surface, suggesting a great antiquity and the passing of much traffic. The Greensand generally only displays its true green colour when freshly exposed by recent digging but green it certainly is, and the name is well deserved. Its other name is Foxmould and when you see its rich rusty brown aspect, this is certainly credible. It can be quite richly fossiliferous too, but more often than not, appears to be quite barren of evidence for past life (Fig. 133). This is partly due to its very porous nature, which permits ground water to flow readily though it, and in turn to dissolve away the shells of the marine creatures that once lived in the waters above this ancient sea-bed. Where shells are preserved they are most commonly of small oysters and these can be extraordinarily numerous; a handful of sand might yield a dozen or more in rich seams. In addition to these humble shellfish, there

Above, Fig. 126: Just south of the City of Bath are these abandoned buildings marking the site of the former mines which worked the Fullers Earth. This clay was the equivalent of the Bath Stone which occurs just a few kilometres further east and north.

Below, Fig. 127: The Forest marble is a tough sandy limestone which forms a gently dipping plateau on the eastern borders of the county, seen here close to Bruton at Seat Hill.

Above, Fig. 128: The Forest Marble used to be quarried for building stone, and the limy beds used for lime making too.

Below, Fig. 129: Forest Marble.

Left, Fig. 130: The Forest Marble was burned in these kilns to provide lime for various purposes.

Below, Fig. 131: This old quarry at Hadspen (near Castle Cary) was dug in the Inferior Oolite. It produced poor quality building stone and limestone for lime making. There are still many fossils, e.g. *Trigonia* and brachiopods, visible in the old tips.

Above, Fig. 132: There are still many fossils, e.g. the bivalve *Trigonia* and the brachiopod *Acanthothyris* , visible in the old tips.

Below, Fig. 133: This bivalve from Penselwood is a species characteristic of the Upper Greensand (*Neithea quinquecostata*).

are some notable giants too, and ammonites over a foot in diameter (30 centimetres for you youngsters) have been found. The Greensand represents a period when the whole area was submerged by a very shallow and warm sea and was rich in life, with both swimming and sedentary animals in quantity.

Chalk; Animal, Vegetable or Mineral?

The Greensand was followed by the deposition of the Chalk, a very well known and consistent horizon of rock, which can be traced from the south coast of east Devon all the way to Yorkshire. High 'downs' mark its position and its thin soils generally support cereal growing or grazing for sheep but not much else. The Chalk does not quite make an appearance in the county of Somerset but it lies very close to this eastern border just above the Greensand and forms the second escarpment on the eastern border. The Chalk is a very fine-grained rock and has little in it to suggest that there were any rivers flowing in the area adjacent to the sea in which it formed, being quite brilliantly white in the upper part. It does have a rather off-white basal layer, the Lower Chalk, and this reflects the small input of land-derived debris that was still reaching the sea after the end of the Greensand deposition, but this soon vanishes and most of the Chalk is devoid of solid grains of land-derived sediment. The environment in which it formed must have been sparkling, clear, turquoise-blue waters above a dazzling white sea-bed. What a pity that England drifted so far northwards after Cretaceous times!

The Chalk is sometimes apparently devoid of fossils and many a quarry or cutting can be examined in vain and yet it does actually contain a rich fauna, and indeed flora. Much of it is hidden from view simply because it is too small to be discernible without a microscope, and consists of the tiny skeletal plates of algae that were a part of the plankton, together with the globular shells of protozoan animals called Foraminifera that also drifted about in the waters above the sea-bed. These tiny skeletons accumulated in vast quantities to form the bulk of the Chalk rock itself, so that all of it can be regarded as being of fossil origin but the macro-fossils are much less common. When they are seen, the commonest are the sea-urchins and these are sometimes quite numerous, but even on a good day it is unlikely that you will find more than half a dozen unless you know exactly where to look. Sometimes the best chance of finding these is to examine the flinty pebbles that weather out of the Chalk because these occasionally formed around the sea-urchins and replicated them. Flint is an extraordinarily tough material which is nigh-on indestructible, so the fossils are often quite clearly recognisable, even after years of exposure to the elements, in ploughed soil, in river gravels, or on beaches.

Flints

Flints are themselves a very curious type of rock. They are not laid down as pebbles in the original sediment but are the result of secondary deposition of their parent material, which is silica, and this forms in the Chalk itself as a sort of cement. However, it seems that Chalk and Flint are two quite incompatible substances and the Flint replaces the Chalk as it forms, so that the Flint occupies a cavity of its own making in the Chalk and will readily fall out of the rock when exposed to weathering. The reason why flints form at all is rather a complex one, resulting from a chemical change in the chalky sediment shortly after its deposition. Chalk is made of pure lime and as such is highly alkaline, being devoid of acidic material. Flint, on the other hand, is solid silica, (Silicon Oxide) which is quite readily soluble in acidic waters but not in very alkaline ones. When ground waters move about they often dissolve some silica and carry this in solution until the conditions become more alkaline, and cause it to be deposited. Water moving though Chalk is naturally very quickly turned alkaline by contact with the lime and most silica will soon be precipitated as a semi-solid substance which is best described as a gel. This soft material is not capable of dislodging solid particles of lime but tends to accumulate wherever there may be voids in the sediment, e.g. in the cavities inside buried fossils, as well as in the pores in between the sediment grains, and may also replace the lime by dissolving it into the water.

Once the silica is precipitated in this way the water surrounding the silica precipitation site is relatively depleted in silica so, to replace it, silica diffuses from the surrounding region in towards the site of precipitation. This creates an inflowing stream of silica and can result in the growth of quite large flint nodules from modest beginnings. Some have been recorded at half a metre and more in diameter, although they are typically a few inches across. The strange and irregular shape of the nodules is also explained by this rather haphazard growth mechanism, which is determined by the relative porosity of the sediment and its chemical state, rather than by any more obvious features such as fossils, or bedding planes. It is true that some flints seem to restrict themselves to the confines of a fossil shell, or are concentrated along the bedding planes of the Chalk, but many more are not.

Flints are not exposed in any significant outcrops within the county boundaries but they are very numerous as residual pebbles weathered out of long vanished Chalk exposures, some of which undoubtedly covered the county, at least in part. These pebbles are seen in almost any stream bed, most soils will contain some, and the coast is also a rich source. This is because of their extraordinary toughness and it is this property that has given them their main value to man, as sources of workable tool-forming stone. Flints are by far the best stone from which to manufacture sharp cutting tools for working wood, bone and leather, and were worked from prehistoric times by peoples of the ancient world, including residents of Somerset. Naturally, the supply of flints was restricted largely to those parts of the country where the Chalk occurred and consequently a trade in raw flint pebbles seems to have been needed. The naturally occurring outcrops of Chalk end in southern Britain around the eastern and southern boundaries of Somerset, and whilst flints can be found occurring quite naturally in streams and on beaches further to the west, the quantity and quality soon diminish, so that imported flints were probably required, at least to make larger tools.

The eastern side of the county is not rich with many readily accessible rock exposures but what it might lack in solid rock, it certainly compensates for in scenery and the region well deserves a visit for this alone. It is probably the least spoiled part of the county, if we exclude the wilder reaches of the far west, and is little changed in character by the twentieth century.

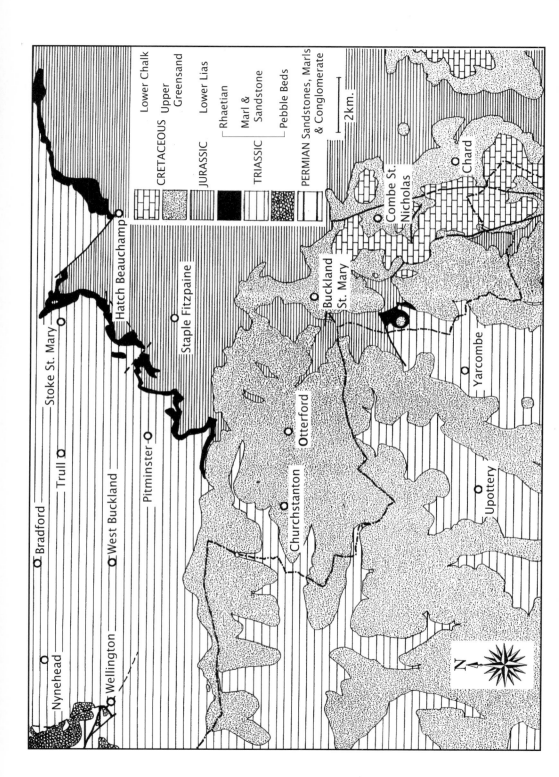

CRETACEOUS
Lower Chalk
Upper Greensand

JURASSIC
Lower Lias

TRIASSIC
Rhaetian
Marl & Sandstone
Pebble Beds

PERMIAN Sandstones, Marls & Conglomerate

2 km.

Nynehead
Bradford
Trull
Stoke St. Mary
Hatch Beauchamp
Staple Fitzpaine
Wellington
West Buckland
Pitminster
Churchstanton
Otterford
Buckland St. Mary
Combe St. Nicholas
Chard
Yarcombe
Upottery

N

The Blackdown Hills

The southern county boundary of Somerset could not be more clearly marked than by the high ground of the Blackdown Hills (Fig. 135). Today, we can drive from the outskirts of Taunton to the top of the hills in a matter of minutes, but before the age of the car these hills, which rise to over 300 metres above sea level, were a formidable barrier to travel. Even when you reach the top, the prospect for a traveller is not encouraging, because settlements are few and mostly hidden from view in deep valleys. The views are fabulous however, and well worth the journey on a clear day. If you look northwards over Taunton Deane from the Duke of Wellington's monument on the southern county boundary, you can see from the Brendon Hills in the west of the county, all the way across the Quantocks to South Wales. From view points south of Taunton you can see round to the Mendips and Glastonbury Tor in the East. From other vantage points you might also look south to the valley of the River Axe running out at Seaton to the English Channel.

As you reach the top of the hills, the extensive plateau that greets you is entirely the result of the nature of the rocks (Fig. 136). The rocks of the Blackdown Hills are the youngest that we shall encounter in Somerset, apart from the Quaternary sediments of the levels, and are of Cretaceous age, that is dating from the period between 135 million and 65 million years ago. The predominant rock is a sandstone known as Greensand, due to the presence of grains of a green mineral called Glauconite. In places this rock has been hardened by the addition of Silica to form a rock called Chert, which is very like flint. Chert is a rock in which the whole body of the rock is composed of silica, not in the usual crystalline form of Quartz, but in a hydrated and amorphous form. Cherts are extremely hard and also resistant to chemical attack, so that the rocks of the Blackdown Hills are almost impregnable to the normal forces of weathering. Thus, whereas all the younger rock which once may have covered them is now

Fig. 134: The Blackdown Hills are flat plateau dominated by the hard chert bands of the Upper Greensand and in the extreme borders of the county there are remnants of the Chalk. These Cretaceous rocks rest unconformably over the eroded Jurassic and Triassic beds. Note the outcrop of the Rhaetian beds which runs underneath the Cretaceous ones at an acute angle.
(This map is drawn from the British Geological Survey 1:63,360 Sheet 311).

eroded away, the cherts remain at the surface defying the elements to break them down. Since these rocks were first deposited as flat beds of sandstone they have hardly been disturbed at all, and today we find them in their original attitude as horizontal beds, which give rise to the extraordinarily flat topped hills (Fig. 137).

Today there are not many rock exposures on the top of the Blackdown Hills, and even around the escarpment they are rare, but in the past the stone was worked for building, and there were therefore many more small pits and quarries. Whilst these are now largely obscured, there are some very fine examples of older buildings with this material facing the walls, and in skilled hands it could be worked into useful square blocks. Amongst these buildings is the church at Wilton in Taunton, which is possibly the oldest church in the town. Here, the blocks of chert are beautifully dressed into small rectangles which, when carefully placed, give an impression of regular ashlar masonry. Similar examples of buildings faced with chert can be found throughout the Blackdown area, anywhere from Chard to Wellington, and give a very distinctive 'look' to the architecture. The larger blocks that were quarried were often quite well bedded, and broke into flat sided blocks quite readily. These were used more or less as they came, and you may find buildings where much of the walling is of this sort (Fig. 138).

Another valuable product of the hills in the past were sharpening stones, used for giving an edge to cutting tools, and notably to scythes. The Blackdown scythe-stone industry was well known before the age of modern synthetic abrasives, and occasional specimens still turn up in junk shops and markets, although the place of origin of these is always open to question. The stones were formed into elongated cigar-shaped objects, and were valued because they combined durability with a gritty abrasive texture, which gave a bite to their action on the steel. The quarries from which they were dug are, like many another, long gone or lost from sight, but their products remain to remind us of them (Fig.139). There is one type of rock which occurs nearby, usually found in the sub-soil around the Taunton area, and that is 'Sarsen' stone. This is a very tough silica-cemented sandstone which is usually found as loose masses in the surface of softer beds. It is clearly a relic from some former bed of rock which has survived weathering and remained as a reminder of the parent rock, now long since destroyed. These boulders often exceed one metre in diameter and a number of them turned up when the M5 motorway was driven past Taunton in the 1970's. They were usually lost in the general confusion of construction but one or two attracted the attention of archaeologists and, since they are more commonly found as the main building stones of prehistoric monuments such as Stonehenge and the Avebury rings, were pushed to one side. These rare stones

Above, Fig. 135: The Blackdown Hills form a strong escarpment which marks the southern boundary of the county near Taunton.

Below, Fig. 136: The Blackdown Hills are flat-topped due to the horizontal beds of Cretaceous Upper Greensand which cap them.

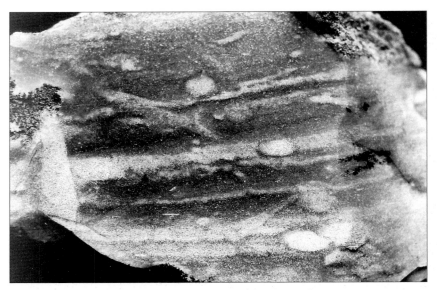

Above, Fig. 137: The Cherts of the Upper Greensand were once sandstones, but have since become silicified and form extremely durable rocks, much used for building.

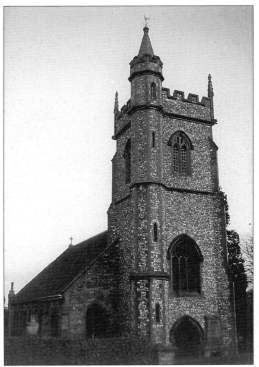

Left, Fig. 138: This fine tower of Wilton Church is faced in small blocks of carefully dressed chert from the Upper Greensand.

Above, Fig. 139: Until the advent of modern synthetic abrasives natural stones were used to make scythe sharpening stones such as these, and the Blackdown Hills was an important local source.

Below, Fig. 140: The Blackdown Hills preserve many varieties of bivalves and other shells, and these highly silicified examples show fine preservation. They have been replaced by silica.

Fig. 141: In the lowest beds of the Chalk which are found close to Chard there are some examples of the marine life of the Cenomanian times. These include this ammonite *Mantelliceras*, sea-urchins such as these *Holaster* and many other shells. Note that the ammonite has preserved small spots of original shell ornament on the final rib close to the aperture of the shell.

are all that remain from some former bed of sediment which was weathered away, perhaps millions of years ago, so if you come across some odd lump of tough sandstone, it may just be a Sarsen.

One of the most notable products of the Blackdown Hills to a geologist, was the wonderfully preserved fossil shells that were found in some of the sandy sediments. The action of silica in solution in the ground water was to infill available spaces in the sands, and thus to convert the rock from sandstone to quartzite or to chert. The same mineral-bearing water could also react with the calcium carbonate of shells and replace it with silica. When this happened, the original shell was entirely replaced so that the original shape was exactly as it was when the animal died, but the internal structure of the shell was lost, and replaced by translucent silica. Since silica is chemically inert, and very tough mechanically, this ensured that the fossils were preserved in minute detail. The silicified shells from the Blackdown Hills are superbly preserved, with every tiny feature of their shape and surface ornament still clear. The collections in Taunton Museum include some very fine specimens, but they are now largely unobtainable in the field, unless you happen across an old hidden quarry (Fig. 140).

Reconstructing the Greensand environment

The cherts described above come from a horizon of rocks known as the Upper Greensand. In many parts of the south of England this horizon is represented by sands which are quite soft and sometimes notably green in colour, although they can also appear rather an orange shade of brown. This green colour is due to the mineral Glauconite, which is today found in shallow warm seas and which is believed to have formed in similar environments in the past. This suggests that the Cretaceous period was one of warm climatic conditions in Britain. The coarse sandstone rocks exposed around Chard show that during the deposition of the Greensand the sea was extremely shallow and the shoreline was probably only a few miles away. In fact it was in east Devon. The sea which covered this area of south Somerset advanced over the land from the east during the early Cretaceous times and did not reach its westernmost limit until near the end of the period. The deposits on the Blackdown Hills, together with those on the Haldon Hills near Exeter, mark the westernmost limits of outcrops of the Cretaceous in southern Britain. However, there is evidence, in the form of flints left behind after weathering of chalk, that this unit of rock used to cover the area to the west, even though it is now devoid of any trace of the Chalk due to its total erosion. At the time of deposition of the Greensand, ie. around 95 million years ago, much of western Britain was still dry land, but by the late Cretaceous, when the Chalk was forming, almost all of Britain was covered by shallow seas

181

and the land was reduced to a few remote and low lying areas in central Wales, the Lake District and Scotland.

Fossils of the Cretaceous period

The shallow warm waters of the Greensand seas were rich in animal life and have yielded a wide selection of fossils, including many bivalve shells, sea urchins and ammonites. These were often found to be crowded together in concentrated layers at the base of some beds of rock, and localities near Chard have yielded many fine specimens from the Greensand/Chalk boundary. These localities are now largely worked out though, so you need to visit local museums to see good material (Fig. 141).

The Tertiary Period in Somerset

With the passing of the Cretaceous period the story of the geology of Somerset was completed for many millions of years. This is because whatever happened afterwards has not left any rocks as evidence. They have all been entirely eroded away from the county. Our present day exposures of rocks tell us nothing about the next 60 million years, and it is not until the era known as the Quaternary, ie. the last two million years, that we have more sediments deposited in the county, mostly over the low land of the Somerset levels. In this long period of time there was much going on elsewhere, but in Somerset it seems that the surface was being eroded rather than deposited, and so we have no rocks remaining to study. The cause of this erosion was that the area was uplifted above sea level, and erosion proceeded to remove much of what had been deposited, leaving us today with the remnants of a once continuous cover of Cretaceous and Jurassic rocks.

One apparent cause of this uplift is not hard to find, because at the end of the Cretaceous period, there was a very important mountain building episode which affected all of Europe, and left us with the newly created Alps. In Britain the effects were very modest by comparison but they include the folding of the rocks of the Dorset coast, giving us the vertical stacks of Portland Stone especially well seen in Durdle Door near Lulworth Cove. In the Isle of Wight, the pinnacles of chalk which form the Needles are another product. In Somerset, the most obvious result was that the land was elevated above the sea and that no more sediment was preserved until the Quaternary period. There is also some post-Jurassic folding and faulting which affects much of the county, the age of which is not always clear. It is probable that some of these structures relate to this Alpine event and the modern variations in topography therefore owe something to the distant Alpine mountain building episode.

There is another explanation however, and this has been developed in recent years by one of the co-editors of the Geological Society's 'Atlas of Palaeogeography and Lithofacies', Dr J.C.W.Cope, a man who knows his Mesozoic rocks very well. He argues that the area most affected by the post-Cretaceous uplift is not the south coast, as you might expect if Alpine earth movements were the cause, but the Irish Sea. It is certainly true that Cretaceous and Jurassic sediments were once deposited much further west and north than they are now seen, and there are still tantalising remnants in Northern Ireland and southern Scotland to prove it. It is around the Irish Sea that these rocks are totally absent and most of the sediments in England dip gently away from this general area. He suggests that there may have been a large-scale uplift centred on this area in the Tertiary era, and the most probable cause of this would be the general volcanism that affected northern Britain at around 50 million years ago. With this explanation we can readily appreciate why the Somerset area is the western limit for many of the Mesozoic rocks; they were once present further west, but have been eroded away during this later uplift.

The Blackdown Hills form a natural barrier on the southern borders of the county, but further east, as on the high ridge of Windwhistle above Crewkerne, they blend in to the undulating country which marks the transition from Somerset to Dorset. Here the geology becomes more varied and the topography reflects the changing rock types.

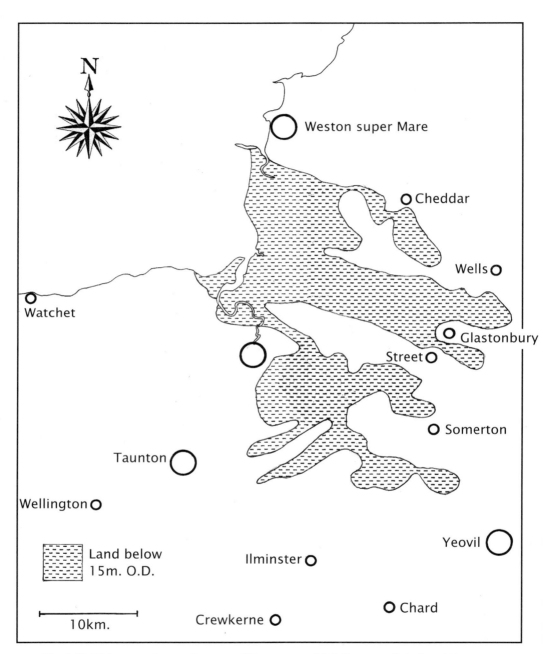

Fig. 142: This map shows the area of Somerset which lies mostly below 15 metres O.D. If the sea were to rise by around ten metres and pumping were to stop, much of this region would be flooded. This happened naturally in the recent past, allowing marine sediments to be deposited over the Somerset Levels.

The Somerset Levels

This region has surely to be the most evocative of Somerset, and is instantly recognisable as somewhere very special, with its own atmosphere and character. The levels are centrally situated in the county, lying between Bridgwater and Glastonbury, and extending to both north and south, covering a total area of hundreds of square kilometres (Fig. 142). The levels could fairly be said to divide into two or even three regions. The Polden Hills bisect them in a low ridge running east to west, and again the Mendip Hills effectively cut off a small region to their north which is similar in character to the main area, but is in effect an extension of the coastal plain which leads into the Chew Valley. We shall concentrate on the area south of the Mendip Hills, which covers the heart of the county and is divided by the low ridge called The Poldens. The levels south of the Poldens are collectively known as Sedgemoor, with areas taking pre-fixes such as West Sedgemoor, and different parts named after local villages, e.g. Aller Moor and Muchelney Level. The peat moors north of the Poldens are also named after local villages, e.g. Mark Moor, Westhay level, Edington Heath and many others.

The geology of the area is remarkably little exposed, even by Somerset standards, and a casual inspection will reveal very little of it. Most of the area is floored by thick peat deposits and no rocks are visible at or near the land surface. On slightly elevated ground there are a few natural exposures, mainly in stream beds, and on rare occasions it is possible to see small areas of rock very close to the land surface where trees have fallen and lifted the entire depth of soil with their roots. This improbable sounding event is largely due to the nature of the geology. The majority of the region of the levels is underlain by the soft sticky clays of the Jurassic lower Lias, which are inter-bedded with thin limestones. The clays readily soften to become heavy, wet soils and the area supports lush summer grazing for cattle on this rich land, but the limestones are so numerous that it is often little more than half a metre down to the first layer of hard rock below the surface, and it is this that weakens the grip of trees on the land. Their roots often spread out through the surface layer of clay, only to be stopped by the first solid limestone that they meet. Thus the roots become matted above the solid rock, rather than penetrating through it, and strong winds easily unseat them and cause all the soil to be lifted cleanly away from the rock. Whilst these tiny exposures are not normally very revealing, they do give us a chance to glimpse the undisturbed geology, and can be useful in the lack of any other evidence. However, the feature of the geology that attracts the attention of all visitors to the area is the superficial deposits that rest on top of the older rocks, that is the peat which now forms the ground surface, resting on the clays and sands that were deposited during the period of the Ice Ages.

Peat

The youngest and most obvious sedimentary deposit of the Somerset levels is the peat which covers their surface (Fig. 143). This dark brown organic material is the product of millennia of accumulation of plant debris in marshy conditions, where the organic matter was incompletely decayed and reduced to a partially rotten state. The bacterial action was slowed by the lack of oxygen, and possibly also by a lack of minerals in the vegetation, and consequently the plant matter was incompletely rotted, so that today it is still possible to see plant fibres and woody structures in the peat, even though all the strength has gone from them. The process is the first in a series of stages which would eventually lead to the formation of coal, and peat is but a stage in the formation of this valuable resource. Coal is of far higher calorific value than peat because it has been much more greatly compressed and has lost its water content, and also because the plant tissues have been further decayed than in peat, so concentrating the most calorific components, the heavier hydrocarbons, and removing the lighter volatile constituents. Peat is potentially a valuable fuel, but it needs to be thoroughly dried out before use and cannot be distilled to give liquid fuels so readily as coal. It is fortunate for Somerset that this is the case, because with the ever increasing demand for fossil fuels at low prices, had this not been so,the peat moors of Somerset would have been far more exploited than they have been. As things are, there is a very small amount of peat dug for fuel, mainly for local consumption, and the vast majority of what is worked goes into soil-less composts.

Drainage and wildlife

These peat workings have given the landscape a lot of its most characteristic features, especially the large areas of open water which can today be visited in places like Shapwick Heath, where they are now part of a nature reserve, managed by English Nature. This open water is on the site of former peat diggings and with modern drainage would not exist today but for them. Large areas of peat moorland have been drained to allow grazing as well as to assist peat digging, but once the digging ceases the water returns to create new habitats for aquatic wildlife which would otherwise not be able to establish itself. Thus, the apparent evils of peat working, which are often cited as the cause of so much

Above, Fig. 143: The central part of Somerset is blanketed by thick beds of peat which when dug away readily flood.

Below, Fig. 144: Meare Heath is sited on peatlands. Some old peat workings are now flooded to form shallow lakes.

Above, Fig. 145: In winter the wetlands can readily revert to being shallow lakes, despite the drainage and pumping.

Below, Fig. 146: The Somerset levels finish abruptly where they meet the former sea-cliff line, now many kilometres inland.

Above, Fig. 147: Hurcot Hill, south of Street, was once at the edge of the flooded area of the Somerset levels and must have formed a sea cliff. It exposes the Triassic rocks, including the pale grey Rhaetic Marls.

Below, Fig. 148: Nyland Hill, south of Cheddar, is an outlying piece of Carboniferous limestone which has withstood the marine erosion that once formed the Somerset levels, so it truly is 'an island'!

Above, Fig. 149: Burrow Mump stands above the surrounding levels as an island, which it clearly once was.

Below, Fig. 150: Westonzoyland and neighbouring villages were built on the elevated land over the Burtle Beds which show up in drought conditions because of their superior drainage.

Above, Fig. 151: The Burtle Beds are marine sands which were deposited by the sea when it flooded central Somerset and they contain modern marine shells, such as the mussels seen here at Othery.

Below, Fig. 152: These Burtle Bed shells are from recent marine sands dug at Greylake, just a few kilometres west of Street.

Above, Fig. 153: The Polden Hills form a ridge which extends from just north of Bridgwater eastwards to Street. It was caused by faulting and elevates the Triassic above the lower Jurassic. (Photo by courtesy of Mick Aston)

Below, Fig. 154: Glastonbury Tor, seen here in the distance surrounded by low ground, has resisted erosion very much better than surrounding rocks, despite being composed of middle Lias clays, sands and limestones. The reason for its survival is probably the local structural geology which may have uplifted it slightly.

Fig. 155: One of the most striking outlying hills in Somerset is Brent Knoll, close to Burnham on Sea. This hill is composed of middle Lias clays, sands and limestones just like those of Glastonbury Tor. Its survival is equally difficult to explain, but it was quite clearly resistant to marine erosion which flattened the surrounding areas.

destruction of wetlands, have in some cases ensured the survival of pockets of wildlife which agriculture alone would long since have done away with. The real enemy of wetlands is drainage of course, and it is this which has to be controlled to establish a part of the levels as a permanent wetland habitat. As it happens, peat digging seems to be in decline at the end of the 20th Century, and the adverse publicity surrounding peat extraction has driven the larger producers to look for alternative sources of organic matter to make composts. Consequently, the old diggings are fast reverting to various stages of wilderness (Fig. 144). It may not be long before the industry is reduced to a few localised pockets of small-scale extraction run by local families and water will invade much of the land once more, but this time with several metres of its upper levels removed! When you consider that the general elevation of the Somerset levels is less than 5 metres O.D. you will realise that any slight increase in water level could have an enormous impact on the ecology of the region and very serious consequences for the local inhabitants (Fig. 145).

Changing sea-levels

The time of the Ice Ages was one of great changes in the otherwise relatively stable climatic environment in Britain and as well as temperature fluctuations, both colder and warmer, the main effect of the freezing and thawing cycles was upon the sea-level. In these days, when global warming seems such an important matter for debate, it is very interesting to have evidence in the geological record for the changes in sea-level that Ice Ages can cause. It is clear from the raised beaches, cliff-lines, caves and sunken forests etc., that the region was one which alternately flooded and dried out (Figs. 146, 147, 148 & 149). In fact this happened several times, due to the changing volume of water locked up in the polar ice caps. The colder the weather, the more water was frozen and deposited on land and the lower the sea-level fell to supply the water. During the warmer interglacial spells, in which the climate would sometimes be a great deal milder than today's, with a balmy almost Mediterranean feel, the sea-level rose and flooded much of what is now land. These changes in sea-level were of great significance in low-lying tracts of land and the Somerset levels owe their nature and name to this flooding in the recent past. During times of high sea-level, such as the last interglacial, the sea brought with it sand, carried in during storms and surges of high water. Other finer grained sediments were deposited from the water during quiet spells. The finest grained muds were possibly deposited by the same rivers that we now see slowly winding their way across the levels, but during times of flooding by the sea they were effectively pushed back to the east and the levels became their estuaries.

Sea shells in Somerset!

The marine deposits from these flood periods are very poorly exposed but can occasionally be seen projecting through the surrounding peat, especially in the area to the east of Bridgwater, where the ridges on which many of the villages are sited, e.g. Othery, Westonzoyland, and famously, Burtle, are made up of marine sands (Fig. 150). If you inspect the soil on these slightly raised mounds you will see that it is not the usual black and sticky peat but light, pale-coloured and sandy, and in excavations it is quite common to find sea-shells of modern species; e.g. limpets, mussels, cockles etc. (Figs. 151 & 152).

Sand

The importance of these mounds of sand in an otherwise flooded marsh must have been immense in pre-drainage times, and it is easy to appreciate why the villages of the levels are crowded on to the raised ground, especially if you drive through the region in the winter after heavy rains. There have been times in the not-too-distant past when you could find temporary exposures of sands in these slightly elevated ridges and their geological name, the Burtle Beds, gives a clue as to the most likely place to look! However, there are not many exposures now and you will need to look very carefully to come across one where the sea-shells are well displayed, although most places will yield a limited selection to prove the marine origin. When deeper cuttings are made into the sands it is surprising to find that some of them are quite firmly cemented into rock. The sands are usually perfectly loose and run through your fingers but occasionally hard balls of sand are found and these can even merge into bands which are cemented into solid limestone with the sand making up the bulk of the rock, but sea-shells are clearly visible in amongst it. There used to be a quarry at Greylake where the sands were visible but this is now overgrown. Temporary exposures are the best hope of seeing this unusual deposit.

The age of these sands is a matter of thousands, rather than millions of years, and it is remarkable that in such a short space of time the sands have been converted from soft sediment into solid rock. This demonstrates very clearly that the age of rocks has little or nothing to do with their hardness. The Chalk, for example, is much older than these limestone concretions in the Burtle Beds and yet is much softer, and the Lias clays which floor the Somerset levels are still very soft sediments in the main, despite being almost 200 million years old.

Mud

There is one other sedimentary deposit on the levels which is of considerable geological significance but is rarely seen. This is a sticky grey clay which lies underneath the peat. It is of estuarine origin and clearly pre-dates the establishment of the peat deposits which followed the last glacial episode. The clay is thick in places, as much as about thirty metres including intermediate sands and peat beds, and itself rests upon the eroded 'solid' geology which underlies the entire region of the levels. It was evidently deposited after a period when the sea-level had been very much lower than today, so eroding the rocks far below the modern levels, and dates back to times between 10,000 years ago, when the seas were as much as thirty metres below today's level, and 5,000 BC when peat formation started. The ground-up rock debris produced by the glaciation was washed by meltwaters on to this deeply eroded surface and eventually was deposited in thick beds, with sea-shells trapped within it as evidence of its marine origin. It was only after this clay had largely filled up the marine basin to around Ordnance Datum that peat formation could start in the marshes. These were created during the warmer interglacial in which we still live, which started about ten thousand years ago. This estuarine clay is topped by a thick peat bed of several metres in depth but north of Wedmore this peat is overlain by another thin (2.5-4.0 metres) clay horizon, dating to around 250 AD, known as the 'Roman Clay'. This clay has very little peat above it, showing that peat formation is largely at a standstill. This Roman Clay accounts for the absence of peat working in the northern part of the levels because there is insufficient depth of peat exposed above the thick clay to merit its extraction.

Rhaetic ridges

The only significant unit of rock which can be found well exposed in the region occupied by the levels is that of the Triassic period. It is best known for the bright brick-red silts and marls which are found in the main body of the Triassic rocks and these form a soft floor to the western parts of the levels, especially in the south around the Curry Rivel region, but the latest rocks of this period are quite different in character and form the harder Rhaetic beds which are seen in the ridge of the Polden Hills. The low ridges of rocks which cross the levels, effectively bisecting them, ie. the Poldens and the Wedmore ridge, are composed of slightly more resistant bands of rock which are from the latest stage of the Triassic, about 207 million years ago.

The Polden Hills and Wedmore ridge are elevated due to structural features in the geology. They should normally be submerged under younger rocks but they were uplifted by gentle folding which affects all of the central Somerset basin and which caused a broad central Somerset anticline, or upward fold. These ridges are the result of local disturbance in the ground which fractured in some places to accommodate the movement, and where one side of the fracture was uplifted, as in the southern side of the Polden Hills, the harder rocks were elevated above the surrounding softer ones and have not yet been reduced back to sea-level (Fig. 153). Most of the isolated hills of resistant rock in the central part of the county are due to elevated tracts of slightly harder rock having been left by erosion. There are some striking examples in addition to the ridges just mentioned, for example, the steep-sided hills of Glastonbury Tor, and Brent Knoll near Burnham on Sea (Figs. 154 & 155). Glastonbury Tor is an interesting example because there is no obvious explanation for why it stands so high above the surrounding flat ground and it has evidently resisted erosion far better than the same rocks which once surrounded it. If you look at the geological map, it becomes apparent that the Tor is actually highly elongated in the south-western direction and this is the underlying trend of its structure. It is also clear that this is exactly the same line as is followed by some major structural faults which cut through the Polden Hills, just a few kilometres away to the south-west. Indeed, there is a slight valley which is precisely aligned with this same ridge, near Asney, just north of Walton at the western end of Street, which may well mark the line of a fault. This same feature cuts through the Polden Hills at Pedwell and is followed by the A361. As you drive along this route you are almost certainly travelling along the fault which is responsible for the extension of the Tor and very likely for the spring waters which emerge from the Holy Well on its flanks, and possibly for the Tor itself! Brent Knoll presents another striking feature of the modern landscape, just as in the past it was undoubtedly a conspicuous offshore island. Again, there is little evidence for why it should have survived erosion so much better than the surrounding area, but strange to say, again there is a fault cutting through the hill, again trending north-east/south-west! It seems remarkable that the two largest isolated hills in the central part of the county should both have strong evidence for faulting associated with them and it surely has some connection with their origins. It has been suggested to me *a propos* the case of Glastonbury Tor (by Prof. Philip Rahtz, pers. comm.) that mineralisation (which I think was conducted by ground waters from these faults), may have been enough to strengthen the rocks, and to enable them to resist erosion. This theory seems to have a lot to commend it, and I am unaware of any better ones.

In time even these impressive hills will be removed and the region will become an uninterrupted sea-washed plain, but only if we cannot prevent a recurrence of the marine flooding which was responsible for creating the present landscape. However, with global warming it is possible that sea-levels will rise to such an extent that we will need dykes, rather like those which protect much of Holland, to keep out the highest tides, and permanent pumping will be required to keep the region free from flooding in wet seasons. The costs of this will naturally have to be weighed against the economic viability of the land and judging from modern trends in agriculture, it would not be altogether surprising if, in the next millennium, some parts of the levels were allowed to revert to their natural state, for both ecological and economic reasons. This has already been done to some extent in any case, in order to preserve the wetlands for wildlife, and a strong economic incentive, coupled with the political desirability of preserving the remnants of this region, will perhaps be sufficient to prevent its total destruction.

Above, Fig. 156: The best known building stones of the county are possibly those from Doulting and *below, Fig. 157:* Ham Hill. Both are still quarried for fine building stone.

Building Stones

The rocks of Somerset are often hidden from direct view by a covering of soil and vegetation, but you can generally expect to see examples of them wherever you go, conveniently piled up in heaps, called buildings! In addition, there are many areas where stone field walls are found and these are almost entirely built from the most cheaply available local stone. Their absence from much of the county is some indication of the rarity, and therefore the high value, of building stone in the region.

The most dependable buildings in which to see local stones are the older ones, built long before the times of concrete blocks and plastic, when stone was really the cheapest readily available durable material. The churches and older village cottages are usually of stone, as are the better quality large houses and, of course, the town houses and municipal buildings. But beware! The wealthier the client the more likelihood there is of exotic stones being imported to satisfy a whim. So the facade of the bank or the building society is often of foreign stone, cut and polished to a glass-like shine, rather than the hand finished rusticity of good local limestone or sandstone.

Despite the relatively low quality of many Somerset stones there are a few notable exceptions which have very considerable reputations and long histories and which can be seen in many prestigious buildings, both within and outside the County. First amongst these must be the Bath Stone, which is so special to that city that it has been discussed in the Chapter which deals with Bath and will be bypassed here. In examining the stones from the rest of the county, we must include the famous Doulting Stone, from the village just outside Shepton Mallet on the Mendip Hills, and perhaps most famous of all is the Ham Stone, from Ham Hill at Montacute, a few miles west of Yeovil (Fig. 156). The Ham stone has been quarried and worked since Roman times at least and can be seen in many fine buildings, especially in the window and door frames and other carefully worked structural elements (Fig. 157).

In the west of the county there are many places from which high quality tough and durable sandstones can be worked and these are widely used in the Quantocks and Brendon Hills. They are often found in combination with the roofing slates which represent the muddier beds from the same geological period but most of these were worked a mile or two from the county borders in north Devon.

And then there is the Draycott Marble, again from the village of that name, this time close to Cheddar on the southern flanks of the Mendips. This stone is widely used throughout Mendip and into the Somerset levels, for lintels and gate posts and many other structural components of buildings, since it readily works into long beams which are far tougher than most other Mendip stones (Fig. 158).

The stones seen in an area are usually a very good indicator of its geology and even where a few incomers might confuse the issue it is generally perfectly possible to get an idea of the local geology by looking at the buildings. However, this becomes far easier and almost invariably very accurate when you restrict your 'mapping' to the field walls. These are hardly ever made from stone brought in from any distance and indeed, if you look carefully at the profile of the field, you will often see remnants of pits where the stone was once dug just a few yards from its place of use. The short distances over which it was carried are demonstrated where two distinct rocks occurring in adjacent regions are used. This situation occurs on the Mendip Hills where sandstones outcrop in the central region of Blackdown (Fig. 159) and limestones around its flanks (Fig. 160). If you follow the walls across this boundary it is fascinating to see just how precisely the stones can mirror the outcrop. In some places the change from light grey limestone to dark brown sandstone is effected within perhaps fifty yards of the actual outcrop junction. This sharpness of definition is not always quite so clear of course, but it makes an interesting diversion to see just how suddenly the stone use can change as you drive across a major geological boundary. You will find remarkable differences not only in field walls, but in buildings too, if you keep a careful look out as you travel through different regions of the county.

The differences in rock types are seen to affect the architectural style as well as the appearance of the stones themselves. This is because some stones will lend themselves readily to breaking in elongate shapes, whereas others are more blocky. Some split into smooth parallel-sided slabs and others can only be used to make rough irregular pieces. Some striking examples would be the slaty rocks of the Brendon Hills, which cleave readily into fairly flat, if somewhat irregular slabs and these give the walls of buildings a distinctly stratified look (Fig. 161). By contrast, the flints and cherts which were used (in desperation?) on the Blackdown Hills and also in the eastern parts of the county, are rarely available in anything more than a fist-sized lump of irregular shape. They have to be trimmed, 'napped' is the correct term I believe, into square-edged lumps and if carefully fitted they can produce a delightful effect when combined with larger blocks of ashlar. There are some extremely elegant examples of buildings finished in this way to be seen on or close to the Blackdown Hills (Fig. 162) and also in the areas in the east of the county, fringing the Chalk outcrops.

Left, Fig. 158: The village of Draycott is a noted source of the limestone breccia from the Dolomitic Conglomerate, locally known as Draycott Marble. It works readily into long pieces which are useful for lintels and gate-posts as well as ordinary walling.

Below, Fig. 159: The Devonian sandstones yield tough slabs of siliceous sandstone which make good walling stone but are difficult to dress into ashlar.

Above, Fig. 160: The Carboniferous limestone is widely used throughout the Mendip region, both for well-dressed ashlar and, as here, for rough field walls.

Below, Fig. 161: This garden wall at Luxborough is a fine example of the use of slate for building.

Left, Fig. 162: Wilton Church in Taunton is constructed of cherts from the Blackdown Hills with Ham Hill stone used for the carved work.

Below, Fig. 163: Many of the houses in Ilminster are built from a combination of the superior Ham Hill stone and this local Middle Lias limestone from Moolham, on the southern outskirts of the town.

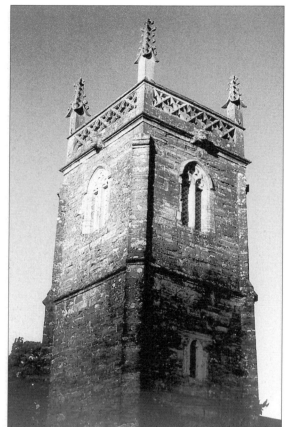

Fig. 164: Doulting stone can be worked into fine masonry and is used for window bars, door frames and carved as here in Stowey church tower, in the Chew valley.

Above, Fig. 165: Dillington House is a fine example of the decorative use of Ham Hill stone.

Fig. 166: The many quarries of central Somerset which once worked the Lias limestone are now represented by those in Charlton Mackerell (above) and Keinton Mandeville (below). Thanks are due to the owners for permission to visit.

Above, Fig. 167: Churches and houses in central Somerset were often constructed largely of flat slabs of the local Blue Lias limestone before the advent of modern building blocks.

Left, Fig. 168: Huish Episcopi Church is a fine example of the use of local Lias limestone with Ham Hill stone.

Above, Fig. 169: Marston Magna used to supply small quantities of an extremely rare stone, crowded with tiny ammonites, which was used ornamentally. Specimens can still be seen inside the local church.

Below, Fig. 170: The Devonian sandstones used in the west of the county as here in Minehead are dressed to rough ashlar blocks, or used as they naturally fracture.

Above: Fig. 171: Merehead Quarry has supplied vast quantities of crushed Carboniferous limestone for the construction industry. Thanks to Foster Yeoman for permission to visit.

Below, Fig. 172: Roofing tiles were always an important requirement of any building and one of the main sources was the thinly bedded sandy limestones of the Jurassic. The largest tiles on the lowest courses of many an old roof are still preserved. This example is the famous 'George Inn' at Norton St. Philip.

Above, Fig. 173: The Devonian slates which were once worked close to Milverton left large spoil heaps.

Below, Fig. 174: The farm buildings at Luxborough were built almost entirely from the local slates. (Thanks are due to the owner for permission to take this photograph.)

Where the local stone is one which only lends itself to being worked into squarish blocks rather than longer pieces, the effect is a curious one, because the two materials are then used in a chequer-board fashion with a panel of flints alternating with a square block of stone, the latter being carefully laid so that adjacent blocks are just seated on the corners of lower ones, leaving a square hole to be infilled with flints. In areas without any good stone, this leads to another distinctive building style where brick is laid in occasional courses with flints, or chert pebbles in between, making a sort of sandwich. The brick courses presumably add strength and stability to an otherwise rather fragile structure. There are few examples in Somerset, most being confined to the extreme south eastern corner where flint and soft stone are the only readily available materials, but it is a more typical feature of the southern half of Wiltshire.

Most reasonably hard stones are used for building in one way or another; for example, the middle lias sandy limestone known as Moolham stone (Fig. 163), but in Somerset there are a few which find favour above others to such an extent that they can be regarded as the main stone for an area. The best examples of these would have to include the Ham Stone and Doulting Stone, both of which are used extensively in the county, the former in the south and the latter in the north. Both stones are worked into window and door frames and other more carefully shaped pieces, since they are both readily obtained in large blocks free from major weaknesses. They are also used for carving into ornamental features and some extremely decorative work has been executed in them, especially that dating from the 15th Century for which Somerset churches are famous (Figs. 164 & 165).

The central part of the county is dominated by the use of Blue Lias limestones. These readily break into flat blocky pieces, ideal for walling and floor slabs but not so useful for carving, although this is by no means unknown. The Blue Lias is in fact a mixture of dark shales and grey muddy limestones which weather quite easily. Older buildings often show deeply corroded stones on the western and southern sides especially, since it is these that experience the wettest weather. The Lias limestone is still hand-worked in the traditional fashion in central Somerset and small quarries near the Fosse Way just south of Glastonbury produce good quality flat blocks, ideal for walling use (Figs. 166, 167 & 168). In the Lower Lias a local speciality, an ammonite-rich limestone, used to be dug at Marston Magna (Fig. 169).

In the north and eastern edge of the county, there are many good limestones including, most famously, the oolitic Bath Stone. In addition to the mines above the City of Bath much of this was quarried in west Wiltshire and the buildings which are made from this pale buff-coloured limestone tend to be found in the area which lies between Bath and Corsham, ie. north of the Doulting Quarries.

There is a belt of country with several good quality buff-coloured stones, including oolites and lime-cemented sandstones, which runs down to the Yeovil area and west towards Chard and this has affected the architecture, giving some of the most mellow and pleasing building materials to be found anywhere. Towns like Crewkerne and Ilminster display these stones at their best and achieve a pleasing overall 'warmth' that could never be found in the Mendip Hills or the Brendons and Quantocks, charming though these also are.

The west of the county is characterised by much older and harder rocks, generally sandstones, but with some muddier slaty rocks too, and these form a belt of excellent and durable building stones which stretches from Porlock and Minehead across towards Taunton and south to Dulverton. In these hilly regions, the stones are tough and resistant to the sometimes harsh weather and they are characteristically laid in tightly fitted layers with their naturally flat-sided slabs carefully placed together. The otherwise hard nature of these building stones is pleasantly softened by their deep, almost wine-red, colour (Fig. 170).

The Mendip region is well served with limestones and sandstones and the light grey buildings of the Mendip Hills are matched by the field walls, which demonstrate that stone was cheap and plentiful enough to be used even for these humble structures. The stone of the Mendips reflects the sometimes harsh conditions which can afflict this highland region. If there is anywhere in central Somerset which can be said to be bleak, it must be here. The heights of the hills are made up of Devonian Sandstones but, perhaps because there are no settlements on these tops, the stone is little used. The vast majority of the local buildings are constructed from limestone. It is often almost white when weathered and can make a good foil to other warmer stones but alone it produces a severe aspect on a dull winter's day.

Modern stone extraction for the construction industry is centred on the Mendip hills, seen here at Merehead (Fig. 171). There is really only one area of the county which suffered from a lack of good stone and that was the Somerset levels. Here there simply was no stone exposed at the surface. Transport costs were evidently enough to dissuade people from importing stone and consequently they used brick. There was a thriving brick industry in the Bridgwater area which still leaves its legacy in the red-brick houses of the town and surrounding region, and a drive through the levels will reveal some interesting examples of houses built from heavy materials on soft foundations!

Whilst looking at the stones of the buildings, do not neglect the rooves. These are nowadays covered by a wide range of materials, but not too long ago they were either thatched or tiled and the tiles can reveal a lot about the local geology. Most modern roof tiles are of cement or slate and prior to that they were typically of terra-cotta, ie. brick, but in the older houses you can still see courses of massive slabs of yellow coloured limestones (Fig. 172). Many of these may derive either from the Ham Hill area, or the eastern fringes of the county, and it appears that many roof coverings were once of stone. Perhaps it is because these stones were quick to deteriorate that only the two lowest courses just above the walls are usually preserved, but there may be another reason why the higher parts of the roof are generally covered by brick tiles, and that is weight. The stone tiles are immensely heavy and to support a roof covered by them alone would require an extraordinarily strong structure. If you travel to the Cotswolds, where this was the common practice, you will see how the roof pitches are very steep, to help to support the mass of stone in the tiles on the roof. In general, this is not seen in Somerset, suggesting that the roof never did have a very heavy covering and was therefore designed to have either thin stone tiles such as slates, or the relatively light-weight clay tiles.

Although the majority of buildings in the county are tiled, there are plenty, especially in the west, which have genuine slated rooves. Slates occur in the Brendon Hills and a few at least were quarried in Somerset (Fig. 173), although many more were found barely one mile over the Devon border, close to the village of Dulverton. These soft grey slates are nowhere near as tough and durable as those found in Delabole, Wales or the Lake District, but they served the local community well enough and outlasted many other materials. They tended to be worked in large sizes, perhaps to help overcome their natural weakness, so rooves covered in them have a rather clumsy look, unlike the almost artificially smooth finish that a good Welsh slate roof can have (Fig. 174).

Postscript

I hope that by now you will have developed a keen interest in the county and its geology and be anxious to get out to see some for yourself. It may be a little daunting at first of course, because it is not always clear just where to start and you will probably want a little assistance. Might I suggest that you consider joining a local group of like-minded people and arrange to go out with them? At the time of writing there are at least two local organisations which you could join and these are based in Bristol and Bath. They are the West-of-England group of the Geologists' Association, known as WEGA, and the Bath Geological Society. You can find details of their addresses from the local public library, or you may like to contact the national Geologists' Association which could also tell you of any other groups with similar interests. Another good source of information would be your local Museum. Those in Wells and Taunton both have good geological collections, and their curators will be able to assist you with local contacts.

Another way to expand your knowledge, to be taken into the field to study rocks with people who know about them and to meet other people who share your interests, is to join an adult education class on geology. These are arranged regularly by local providers, and offer a range of activities from local excursions to evening and weekend lectures. They might also lead you to study geology further afield, and there are even field-trips based in remote areas of the British Isles and abroad.

I would like to end on a note of encouragement for those who are just starting to study geology. It is often seen by people in your position as a difficult subject, with lots of technical jargon and a requirement for knowledge of chemistry and physics, but please do not be put off by these thoughts. Much of the fundamental knowledge of geology was obtained by patient observation, using nothing more than a hand-lens and a notebook to record the observations and it was done by people who possibly knew less science than you do, if only because so little was known in their day! So it is perfectly possible for anyone who has a discerning eye to make valuable observations and to contribute to our total knowledge. All that is required is the time and effort to do it. Don't be discouraged, but have confidence and make a start.

Glossary

Many of the terms used in this book are rigidly defined, and can be looked up in geological texts and dictionaries. However, it might be helpful to have a handy reference to save time, and the intention of including a glossary with this book is to save you from the inconvenience of not having an immediate explanation. It may well be that some of the terms simply defined here will be better and more fully explained elsewhere, so please do not be discouraged from further reading. There is a list of books that you might find interesting and helpful in the bibliography.

All dates are taken from the 'Atlas of Palaeogeography and Lithofacies', Geological Society Memoir No.13, 1992, Editors: J.C.W. Cope, J.K. Ingham and P.F. Rawson. NB. Millions of years are represented by Ma.=

Agate This fine-grained stone is usually banded and grey-coloured, but may be stained red or other tints. It is composed of silica and water and forms in cavities, usually in igneous rocks.

Algal Refers to the prime agent responsible for the formation of laminated limestones, the Blue/Green algae.

Ammonite Cephalopod molluscs with coiled plane-spiral shells which lived in the sea during the Jurassic and Cretaceous times, after which they became extinct.

Anhydrite This is a mineral comprised of Calcium sulphate but, as its name implies, without any water. The equivalent hydrated mineral is Gypsum. When roasted this reverts to Anhydrite, when wet this turns back into Gypsum.

Anion This is an elementary particle which carries a negative electric charge and therefore is attracted to the positive electrode (the Anode) and to positively charge ions (Cations).

Anticline A fold which bends upwards, as an arch.

Aragonite This is Calcium carbonate in a mineral form which crystallises differently from Calcite. It is meta-stable, ie. it will revert to Calcite over long (geological) periods of time. It is often the original mineral to precipitate in the sea and may form parts of some shells, especially molluscs.

Armorican One name for the episode of earth movement which followed the Carboniferous in southern Britain.

Ashlar The name of squared and smooth surfaced blocks of masonry used to build panels of walling.

Bedding This is the natural layering acquired by sediments as they are deposited.

Belemnite A cephalopod mollusc with a heavy bullet-shaped skeletal component; it lived in Britain in Jurassic and Cretaceous times and was ancestral to Cuttle-fish.

Bivalves These animals were resident in both sea and fresh waters from early Palaeozoic times until the present, and have two shells, made from carbonate, and usually these are mirror images of each other, but not invariably, e.g. the oyster family.

Blue Lias This is the sequence of dark grey muds and limestones found at the base of the Jurassic in England, and includes ammonites, the definitive first indicators of the Jurassic system.

Brachiopods This Phylum of shellfish is a major component of the fossil record in Carboniferous times when there were eight major Articulate classes but only two classes of Articulate Brachiopods survived into the Mesozoic, the Rhynchonellids and the Terebratulids.

Breccia This is a rock made up of angular fragments of stone set in a matrix of finer material, or purely crystalline cement. It is the lithified equivalent of a scree.

Calcrete The natural equivalent to concrete formed by the replacement of siliceous sediment with lime, to form nodular masses of limestone with relic grains and lumps of the original clastic sediments.

Caledonian The episode of earth movements seen in Northern Britain which occurred at the close of the Silurian Period, about 410 Ma.

Carbonate This is an anion, formed from Calcium and Oxygen, with the formula CO_3.

Carboniferous The period of time which started around 345 Ma and closed with the Hercynian Orogeny around 295 Ma.

Cation This is an elementary particle which carries a positive electric charge, and therefore is attracted to the negative electrode (the Cathode) and to negatively charged ions (Anions).

Cenozoic This is the final major Era, commencing with the Paleocene around 65 Ma.

Chalk This sediment is almost 100% Calcium carbonate and the mineral form is Calcite. It formed in warm seas with no input of clastic sediment, and is composed of extremely small particles, many of which are derived from the plates of algae called Coccolithophores, known as 'Coccoliths'.

Clastic The grains of a sediment are either solid particles, in which case it is clastic, or precipitates of minerals formed in situ or close by, such as some limestones and evaporites.

Clay This term needs definition. It is strictly only applied to silicate minerals which are formed during the process of weathering and which are microscopically small.

Cleavage This is the natural splitting property of rocks, usually acquired when they have been metamorphosed. The same term is applied to minerals.

Coal Measures The sequence of rocks in the Upper Carboniferous which include coal seams.

Conchoidal This term describes the shell-like appearance of fractures formed in substances when they are free from natural flaws. They then break along stress lines determined by the blow they suffer. Flints can be carefully formed by exploiting their tendency to do this. The broken surfaces are usually either convex or concave.

Conglomerate This is a rock formed from pebbles set in a matrix, usually of sand or silt, but sometimes of crystalline mineral.

Cornstone A carbonate-cemented rock found in irregular masses in evaporites.

Cretaceous The Period commencing around 135 Ma. and ending the Mesozoic Era at ca. 65 Ma. Named for its unique thickness of Chalk.

Crinoids A group of echinoderms with a stalk connecting them to the sea-bed and a small body to which radiating feathery 'arms' were attached. One common Jurassic form appears to have been free-drifting.

Devonian The oldest Period which is well represented in Somerset, commencing around 410 Ma. and finishing at around 350 Ma.

Diachronous The concept of time relating to a bed of rock is not always accurate; some beds cross-cut time horizons and are diachronous.

Dip This is the angle at which beds of rock are inclined from the horizontal.

Dolomite This mineral has equal amounts of Calcium and Magnesium ions, combined with carbonate. It is slightly denser than Calcite which it often replaces.

Echinoderms These are another Phylum of animals, entirely marine, which possess external skeletons. They include the sea-urchins, starfish, crinoids and other less commonly preserved groups.

Escarpment The edge of a hill, where the harder rocks are weathering away to cause a sudden steepening of the slope of the ground.

Evaporite A rock sequence , or a mineral, which originated in arid climatic conditions.

Facies This sums up all the visible characters of a rock, its composition, texture and any other distinctive aspects which enable its recognition.

Fault This is a fracture in the rocks along which some movement has occurred. It may be sideways or vertical and any angle in between. Common (normal) faults are caused by stretching of the rocks, others (reverse or thrust) are compressional, and some (tear or wrench) simply accommodate sideways slipping.

Feldspar This is a widespread silicate mineral, formed in igneous rocks and sometimes found as residual grains in sands, especially those weathered incompletely, such as desert deposits.

Fissile The property of splitting readily along pre-determined weaknesses, as in slate.

Glauconite A Calcium-rich silicate mineral formed in warm saline waters and found in shallow marine sediments. It is characteristically green in colour, and easily recognised in hand specimens of rock.

Goniatites A group of cephalopod molluscs which were ancestral to ammonites.

Greensand A sandy sediment with a significant proportion of grains of Glauconite, a green-coloured silicate mineral.

Gruffy ground This is the local name for land which has been dug by miners and is covered by hollows and spoil heaps.

Haematite The oxide of Iron which appears as a striking red stain wherever it occurs. Its true colour when massive is steely-blue/black. It forms in arid conditions, so some desert sands are coated with it.

Hercynian One name for the episode of earth movement which followed the Carboniferous in southern Britain.

Horizon In geological use, horizon is a bed of rock which appears to represent one time or episode.

Horsetails The group of plants with hollow segmented stems from which leaves radiate in rosettes.

Hypersalinity A high degree of salinity which exceeds the normal level of sea-water, generally reducing the life forms which can survive.

Igneous Rocks which derive from melted magma.

Isostasy This is the automatic compensation mechanism which causes the surface level of the land to rise or fall dependent upon the weight of the total rock column. If the surface is eroded then the weight will fall and the land will rise, and if sediment is deposited the weight rises and the surface sinks. It is caused by the buoyancy of the crust on the plastic mantle underneath.

Jurassic A geological Period of time, starting at around 204 Ma and ending around 135 Ma.

Karst A region of the Balkans where limestone is deeply weathered into a characteristic surface. It gives its name to this type of feature wherever it is seen.

Lagoon A shallow and extensive body of sea-water with relatively little connection with the open sea, often warmer and more saline than the main body of the sea, with restricted life forms in extreme cases.

Lava The surface erupted liquid products of melted magma.

Lias The oldest Epoch of the Jurassic, 204-180 Ma. The term is also used to describe the typically alternating layers of clays and limestones found at this horizon in England.

Lignite This is the intermediate stage in the transformation from peat to coal. Lignite is a dark brown slightly flaky substance, not unlike really tough shoe leather after a few years in the garden!

Lime This is the name often given to carbonate minerals, especially Calcium carbonate, which normally crystallises as Calcite. In building terms, lime is actually roasted Calcite, which gives Calcium oxide (Quicklime), and this is then hydrated with water to give slaked lime, Calcium hydroxide.

Limestone A sedimentary rock composed of carbonates, mainly of Calcium or Magnesium.

Lithofacies The same as Facies. This term reflects the sum of the characters of a rock. See Facies.

Lithology This term summarises the total properties of a rock, such as its mineral content, its texture and fabric.

Lithosphere The outer shell of the earth is more or less rigid rock, known as the lithosphere.

Macerals The organic equivalent of minerals which are the components of coal.

Mantle The largest part of the earth, which underlies the crust. It is believed to flow slowly under the influence of convection currents and is responsible for the surface crustal movements, and Isostasy.

Marble This is a limestone which has re-crystallised due to heat and pressure during metamorphism.

Marl A sediment made up of fine clastic particles with lime cement in significant quantity.

Massive This term refers to rocks without conspicuous layering or divisions.

Mesozoic The Era of time which commenced with the Triassic at around 250Ma. and ended with the Cretaceous at about 65 Ma. The name derives from the presence of fossils, indicating animal life, which are neither the oldest, nor the youngest, but in the middle.

Metamorphism This is the process by which rocks are altered underground, under the influence of heat and pressure.

Mica This is a silicate mineral, commonly formed in granite and found as a detrital grain, especially in water-lain sands.

Mineralisation The process in which minerals are deposited in available spaces within earlier rocks, or by replacing the original rock.

Minerals Substances of natural inorganic origin which have fixed composition and structure.

Molluscs This Phylum of animals is a most important group of fossils because they mostly had hard carbonate shells which preserved relatively well in sediments. It includes bivalves, ammonites and gastropods (snails), in addition to other rarer groups.

Nodules These are rounded masses of harder than usual sediment, generally cemented by lime, but may include other minerals, e.g. phosphates and silica.

Ochrous The term used to describe heavily stained sediments, such as clays and limestones, when they contain iron hydroxides of yellow, orange/ brown or red colours.

Ooid The correct term for the spherical pellets of lime formed by the action of Blue/ Green algae, see Oolith.

Oolitic Ooliths, or Ooids as they should be called, are spherical pellets of lime, made by the accretionary accumulation of layer upon layer due to the growth of Blue/ Green algae.

Ores Minerals which are capable of being economically worked.

Orogeny The process of mountain building, which is driven by underlying currents in the mantle of the earth.

Outcrop This is the geographical area where the rock actually meets the surface of the ground (discounting the superficial cover of soil etc.).

Palaeogeography Simply the geography of the world in ancient times.

Palaeozoic This Era, which starts with the Cambrian at around 545 Ma., was named because it was the period of time in which the first animal fossils used to be known. Some animals have been found below the Cambrian boundary however. The Palaeozoic finishes with the Permian Period.

Permian The Period which follows the Carboniferous and marks the end of the Palaeozoic Era at its close, from ca. 295-250 Ma.

Pillow Lava The type of lava which erupts under water and cools into a rounded mass which moulds itself over others of the same form, giving a pile of sack, or pillow-like forms.

Pinnate A leaf which is divided into separate portions along its central stalk, or petiole.

Pleistocene The earlier part of the Quaternary, it started at 2 Ma. and closed with the onset of 'modern' times, the Holocene, around 10,000 years ago.

Pseudomorphs When a crystal is dissolved to leave a hole which is infilled by some other material, the resulting replica is called a Pseudomorph.

Quartz The mineral formed from pure silica; it is the commonest sand particle in clastic rocks.

Quartzite Rock which is principally composed of the mineral quartz, generally resulting from the fusion of sand grains which originally formed a sandstone, either by intergrowth, or silica cement.

Quaternary The Period of the last 2 Ma. of earth history, dominated by the Ice Ages in Britain. Named as the fourth great sub-Era (after the Tertiary).

Radiometric The measurement of radioactivity which is used to determine the age of a mineral.

Regression The retreat of the sea from coastal waters to expose new land.

Rhaetic The final Age of the Triassic Era, starting around 207 Ma and merging almost imperceptibly into the lowest Jurassic in Somerset. Correctly known as the Rhaetian.

Sarsen An isolated stone of silica-cemented sands which is of substantial size.

Scree A loose deposit of sharp-edged stones derived from a hillside, usually stacked at steep angles.

Seatearth The sediment which underlies a coal seam, generally pale-coloured and with rootlets.

Sedimentary Rocks which started off as loose sediment and were consolidated.

Shales Sedimentary rocks made up of clay minerals, always well-laminated and fissile.

Silica The basic component of all silicate minerals, the compound of Oxygen and Silicon with a formula of $SiO2$, which is the sole mineral ingredient in Quartz and sediments such as Flint and Chert.

Silicate This is the Anion $SiO_{2,2}$, the component which defines certain minerals as belonging to one large group, the Silicates, and which attracts positively charged Cations to form minerals.

Silicified Sediments or fossils which started off as another mineral, e.g. Calcite, can be replaced by Silica in solution, which accurately mimics the original shape, leaving a Silicified replica.

Silt This sediment is neither mud nor sand, but in between.

Silurian The Period which contains the oldest Somerset rocks, the lavas at Moons Hill, started at 435 Ma. and finished around 410 Ma.

Slate This rock is mudstone which has been metamorphosed and in the process it acquired a splitting property known as cleavage. This causes it to split through the natural bedding.

Stoping The process of cutting away the roof in a mine to extract the ore or coal.

Stratigraphy The chronological sequence of rocks is represented by a series of names for each separate unit. The total list is the Stratigraphic column, so stratigraphy is the study of this sequence.

Stromatolite The name for a mass of algal limestone which forms into a cylindrical growth, usually a mound, but may be a column.

Symbiotic A relationship between organisms which is mutually beneficial.

Syncline A fold which bends downwards, as a trough.

Tectonic The structural disturbances which affect the rocks of the earth's crust are called tectonic.

Tertiary The sub-Era which follows the Mesozoic Era. This term is often applied to all the youngest rocks but should omit the Quaternary, which is, like the Tertiary, found within the Cenozoic Era.

Thixotropic A curious property which allows particles to bind together when left undisturbed but remain fluid whilst in motion. In practice, clays will flow like water until they settle, when they become stiff and semi-rigid. Cornflour mixed in very little water demonstrates this very well. It can be swiftly picked up as a lump on a spoon, yet will flow off it like cream.

Topography This is the physical aspect of scenery; the shape of the landscape.

Transgression The advance of the sea over areas that were land.

Trilobite The trilobites were arthropods, (jointed-limbed animals) and apparently entirely marine. They lived in the Palaeozoic Era, and became rare in the lower Carboniferous.

Tuff Fine-grained volcanic ash which is solidified into rock.

Type The first recorded occurrence of any fossil species is always illustrated by the 'Type' specimen which is unique and with which all others have to be compared.

Unconformity This is a surface at which the lower rocks are eroded, often after tectonic disturbance and tilting, and on which another younger set of sediments are deposited.

Variscan One name for the episode of earth movement which followed the Carboniferous in southern Britain.

Veins Infilled cracks in the ground with minerals deposited on their walls.

Wadi In desert landscapes, valleys are rarely wet and are often deeply cut as gorges through the solid rock. These are called Wadis.

White Lias The local name for pale creamy-grey limestones and their intervening clays, which occur overlying the red marls of the Triassic. It has no ammonites. NB. This unit is apparently the topmost part of the Triassic system in the UK, despite its rather misleading name. 'Lias' is a term usually taken to mean the lowest Jurassic, but is actually also used as an indicator of the rock types, ie alternating layers of limestones and clays.

Bibliography

The following list includes texts referred to in the book, in addition to a few extra titles which might be found particularly useful. For good accounts of the general geology the best source is likely to be the regional memoirs produced by the British Geological Survey, and their maps are also extremely informative.

'Atlas of Palaeogeography and Lithofacies', *Geological Society Memoir No.13*, 1992, Editors: J.C.W. Cope, J.K. Ingham and P.F.Rawson.

Bath Stone, a quarry history by J.W.Perkins, A.T. Brooks & A.E.McR. Pearce, 1979, University College Cardiff & Kingsmead Press, Bath.

British Mesozoic Fossils, British Museum (Natural History) HMSO.

British Palaeozoic Fossils, British Museum, (Natural History) HMSO.

Coal Mining in Bishop Sutton North Somerset c.1799-1929 written and published by W.J. Williams, 1976.

Old Mendip by Robin Atthill, 1964, published by David and Charles.

The Rocks of Brown's Folly by R.B.J. Smith, published by Bath Geological Society.

The History of the Somerset Coalfield by C.G.Down and A.J. Warrington, published by David and Charles.

British Regional Geology: Bristol and Gloucester Region, 3rd Edn. 1992, British Geological Survey, HMSO.

British Regional Geology: South West England, 4th Edn. 1975 British Geological Survey, HMSO.

British Geological Survey 1:250,000 Sheets 50N04W and 51N04W

British Geological Survey 1:63,360 Sheets 264, 265, 280, 281, 297 and 311.

British Geological Survey 1:50,000 Sheets 278, 279 and 295.

In addition to the geological maps of the county there are several geological memoirs available to accompany the individual maps, e.g. Weston-super-Mare, Bristol, Wells and Cheddar and Bridport and Yeovil. All of these are published by HMSO.

INDEX